Linear Algebra and Geometry

Linear Algebra and Geometry
A SECOND COURSE

Irving Kaplansky

UNIVERSITY OF CHICAGO

Allyn and Bacon, Inc.

Boston

to Spike, Danny, and Lucy

PREFACE

Linear algebra, like motherhood, has become a sacred cow. It is taught everywhere; it is reaching down into the high schools and even the elementary schools; it is jostling calculus for the right to be taught first.

Yet all is not well. The courses and books all too often stop short just as the going is beginning to get interesting. And classical geometry, linear algebra's twin sister, is a bridesmaid whose chance of getting near the altar becomes ever more remote. Generations of mathematicians are growing up who are on the whole splendidly trained, but suddenly find that, after all, they do need to know what a projective plane is.

At the University of Chicago we have for years offered two quarters of linear algebra. In the second quarter there is time to push on to something more advanced. Whenever I have taught this course I have presented various subsets of the material in Chapters 1 and 2.

We offer one quarter of geometry. At present no one is required to take it. There has been an inexorable tendency to assume that the customers have had ever more linear algebra. Chapter 3 represents my answer to the problem: given a roomful of students who have been crammed full of linear algebra, what geometry should you teach them, and how?

I have been a little arbitrary, but I hope not excessively so, in the selection of topics. I touch on similarity lightly because current books are especially strong there. I cautiously stay away from dual spaces for a while, to keep the opening of the book quite elementary, but then use them enthusiastically. Inner product spaces get VIP treatment because I think they are enormously important. Topics related to convexity (Frobenius's theorems on positive matrices, Farkas's theorem of the alternative for two-person zero-sum games, etc.) are omitted entirely, because there I felt least able to make a contribution.

I realize I am not alone in trying to reunite the threads linking algebra and geometry. Let me mention in particular the splendid book of Gruenberg and Weir [15]; I highly recommend it to readers (as a prelude to mine, of course).

I owe a great deal to a great many people. Among outstanding debts that are a pleasure to acknowledge I would like to mention the papers and books of Dieudonné and Jacobson, which taught me so much about inner product spaces, the classic [17] of Halmos on finite-dimensional Hilbert spaces that has since been shamelessly cribbed by everyone (including me), and the geometry courses I took from H. S. M. Coxeter at the University of Toronto. (I hope he will enjoy the enthusiasm he did so much to instil, and forgive the defects.) Priscilla Mao did a fine job on the typing. I am grateful to Mrs. Sylvia Clark and Mr. Gerald Curtis of Allyn and Bacon for their splendid cooperation. My final thanks go to the stream of able students at Chicago who did so much to help shape the book.

IRVING KAPLANSKY

A Note on Prerequisites

I gaze with envy and despair at books by my colleagues, which are organized with meticulous precision, leading step-by-step to a grand climax. The topics I wished to cover did not fall into such a logical pattern. There is a lot of independence among the sections, and I doubt whether an exact description of whatever dependence there is would be worthwhile.

I assume the reader to be comfortably acquainted with the elements of linear algebra, done in coordinate-free style starting with abstract vector spaces. For one who thinks only in terms of n-ples, there will be a problem of translation that will probably be found excessive, and an investment in relearning the foundations (it can be reasonably brief) would be profitable.

I have endeavored to make §§1-1–1-13 quite accessible, granted this much preparation. In §1-14 I indicate how dual spaces can be used to streamline some of the proofs. Of course this section can be omitted. Dual spaces also make a fleeting appearance in §2-2, and their use at this point can be easily circumvented. It is in Chapter 3 that dual spaces are applied in a serious way. The whole discussion of duality in projective spaces will be blurred if another language is substituted for dual spaces.

Section 1-15 is an isolated one. It contains a number of illustrations, which I find attractive, of the interplay between algebra and the extra room for maneuvering one acquires in an infinite set.

Section 1-16 is also isolated, and contains a highly personal selection of theorems on forms over rings. While the background needed on rings and modules is slight, the reader will probably feel a need for the extra maturity acquired during some previous study of ring theory.

Those who think that all fields have characteristic zero will of course skip §§1-6, 1-10, 1-12 (but they may be sorry some day). I have more sympathy for anyone who substitutes the field of real numbers for the real-closed field dominating §§2-1–2-5. Anyway, Tarski has shown us that the kind of theorem occurring here is true for all real-closed fields if it is true for the field of real numbers. So it is not extra generality I seek; it is rather my way of telling the reader, "Make R the field of real numbers if you like, but be warned that the arguments are going to be purely algebraic."

Section 2-5 requires some acquaintance with (non-commutative) ring theory. Otherwise: read and enjoy the theorem, but skip the proof.

When geometry begins in Chapter 3, the level of difficulty of the linear algebra drops by an order of magnitude. As the work comes to a close the theorems fade away in favor of hand-waving on a large scale. But that is the way every course should finish.

The exercises are, by and large, not routine ones. (Warning: the absence of a hint does not necessarily mean that the exercise is easy!) A teacher may find it advisable to add some supplementary exercises. I have occasionally been guilty of using the exercises as an integral part of the text. It is my firm belief that a reasonably diligent reader or student will not find this an obstacle.

CONTENTS

3   GEOMETRY

Linear Algebra and Geometry

1

INNER PRODUCT SPACES

1-1 Definitions and Examples

The fundamental concept in this chapter is that of a *symmetric bilinear form*.

Let K be a field, V a vector space over K. Until §1-15 our main concern will be with the finite-dimensional case, but we allow infinite-dimensionality, and state the theorems in maximum generality; (e.g., in Theorem 2, V is allowed to be infinite-dimensional but the subspace S must be finite-dimensional).

Normally our notation will be early letters of the alphabet for scalars (elements of K), and late letters for vectors. We consider a function of two variables, each of the variables ranging over V, with the values of the function lying in K. Our notation for the function will usually be (,); but when desirable we shall use a functional symbol such as $f(,)$, $g(,)$.

The assumptions are, in brief, symmetry and linearity in each variable. In detail:

(1) $$(x,y) = (y,x)$$

(2) $$(ax + by, z) = a(x,z) + b(y,z)$$

Thus we are explicitly assuming only linearity in the first variable. But (1) and (2) combine to imply linearity in the second variable as well:

$$(z, ax + by) = a(z,x) + b(z,y)$$

We shall usually call the form an *inner product*, and we speak of the structure consisting of V together with the form as an *inner product space*.

We offer a suggestion to the reader: whenever he is faced with a new concept he should check to see whether there are any examples, however trivial. In that spirit we offer as a first example the inner product (defined on any V) that is 0 for all vectors: $(x,y) = 0$ for all x,y in V.

Next we mention one of the main motivating examples. With K the field of real numbers, we think of ordinary Euclidean space; (x,x) is the square of the length of x, and (x,y) is the scalar product of vector analysis (the product of the lengths of x and y and the cosine of the included angle). We shall return to this example in §2-1.

Our further discussion of examples will be in terms of a basis of V, and will be, in effect, a construction of all examples. Let then $u_1, \cdots, u_n$ be a basis of V. Write $(u_i,u_j) = a_{ij}$. Note that by the symmetry of $(\ ,\ )$ we have $a_{ij} = a_{ji}$. A typical element x of V has the form $x = x_1u_1 + \cdots + x_nu_n$. (We violate our convention concerning early and late letters of the alphabet when we take the coordinates of a vector relative to a basis.) If $y = y_1u_1 + \cdots + y_nu_n$ is a second element, we find from the bilinearity

$$(3) \qquad (x,y) = a_{11}x_1y_1 + a_{12}x_1y_2 + \cdots + a_{ij}x_iy_j + \cdots + a_{nn}x_ny_n$$
$$= \Sigma a_{ij}x_iy_j$$

Conversely, we may take a_{ij} to be any elements of K subject to the condition $a_{ij} = a_{ji}$, define (x,y) by (3), and obtain an inner product space.

In a way this is a description of all inner product spaces, but there is more to be said (in fact a good deal more), for we would like to know how the a_{ij}'s are affected by a change of basis.

For this purpose we first introduce the matrix (a_{ij}); let us write it A. We note that it is an $n \times n$ symmetric matrix with entries in the field K. We call it the *matrix of the form* relative to the basis $u_1, \cdots, u_n$.

Now let a second basis $v_1, \cdots, v_n$ of V be given. We express the second basis in terms of the first:

$$v_1 = p_{11}u_1 + p_{12}u_2 + \cdots + p_{1n}u_n$$
$$\vdots$$
$$v_n = p_{n1}u_1 + p_{n2}u_2 + \cdots + p_{nn}u_n$$

Here the elements (p_{ij}) form an $n \times n$ non-singular matrix for which we write P. For the inner product (v_i, v_j) our notation is b_{ij}, and this gives us a second $n \times n$ symmetric matrix B. Now comes a computation, which is brief when written under summation signs, but perhaps a little indigestible:

$$b_{ij} = (v_i, v_j)$$
$$= (\sum_k p_{ik} u_k, \sum_m p_{jm} u_m)$$
$$= \sum_{k,m} p_{ik} a_{km} p_{jm}$$

Now $\sum_k p_{ik} a_{km}$ is (by the definition of matrix multiplication) the i,m-term of the matrix PA. Let us write c_{im} for $\sum_k p_{ik} a_{km}$. Then the remaining sum to be evaluated is $\sum_m c_{im} p_{jm}$. In order to recognize this as a matrix product we have to transpose the matrix P. To see this in detail, write $p_{jm} = q_{mj}$ and regard q_{mj} as the m,j-entry of a matrix Q. Then $\sum_m c_{im} p_{jm} = \sum_m c_{im} q_{mj}$ is the i,j-entry of PAQ. Now Q is the transpose of P, for which our notation will be P'. The upshot of all this is the equation

(4) $$B = PAP'$$

Remark. For a discussion in a more conceptual style, see §1-14.

The matrix relation (4) just encountered deserves recognition on its own merits, and so we define it for any (not necessarily symmetric) square matrices.

Definition. Two $n \times n$ matrices A and B are *congruent* if there exists a non-singular matrix P such that $PAP' = B$.

To show that congruence is an equivalence relation will be left as an exercise (Ex. 1, page 4). However, we should also note that it follows from the above discussion that congruence is an equivalence relation, at least on symmetric matrices; if we had carried through our discussion for general bilinear forms (i.e., not necessarily symmetric ones) the remark would apply to congruence of arbitrary matrices.

We next introduce the concepts of radical and non-singularity.

Let (,) be a symmetric bilinear form on a vector space V. The set of vectors x satisfying $(x, V) = 0$ $((x, y) = 0$ for all y in $V)$ is called the *radical* of the form. It is routine to see that the radical is a subspace. When the radical is 0, we say that the form is *non-singular*. The theory of general inner product spaces can be reduced to non-singular ones. (See Ex. 2 or Ex. 3, page 4.)

We proceed to relate non-singularity of an inner product to non-singularity of the matrix attached to it.

Theorem 1. *Let V be a finite-dimensional vector space over a field K, and let (,) be a symmetric bilinear form on V. Let $u_1, \cdots, u_n$ be a basis of V and let $A = (a_{ij})$ be the matrix determined by the form relative to this basis: $a_{ij} = (u_i, u_j)$. Then (,) is non-singular if and only if A is non-singular.*

Proof. We prove instead the equivalent statement that (,) is singular if and only if A is singular.

Suppose the matrix A is singular. Then there exist elements $c_1, \cdots, c_n$ in K, not all 0, such that the linear combination of the rows of A with coefficients $c_1, \cdots, c_n$ is 0. Write $x = c_1 u_1 + \cdots + c_n u_n$. Then for every i we have $(x, u_i) = 0$. Thus x is a non-zero element in the radical.

The proof of the converse merely requires retracing these steps. Suppose the form is singular, so that there is a non-zero element x in the radical. Write $x = c_1 u_1 + \cdots + c_n u_n$, and note that the c's are not all 0. Then $(x, u_i) = 0$ for all i. This translates to the statement that the rows of A are linearly dependent via the coefficients $c_1, \cdots, c_n$. Hence A is singular.

EXERCISES

1. Prove that congruence of matrices is an equivalence relation.

2. Let V be an inner product space, N its radical. Write $\bar{V}$ for the quotient space V/N. For $\bar{x}, \bar{y}$ in $\bar{V}$ define $(\bar{x}, \bar{y})$ by taking representatives x, y in V and setting $(\bar{x}, \bar{y}) = (x, y)$.
   (a) Prove that $(\bar{x}, \bar{y})$ is well-defined.
   (b) Prove that in this way we get an inner product space on $\bar{V}$ and that it is non-singular.
   (c) Show that the inner product space V is uniquely determined by $\bar{V}$ and the dimension of N.

3. (This is a less invariant but more "down to earth" version of Ex. 2.) Let V be an inner product space with radical N. Let W be a vector space complement of N. Show that the inner product is non-singular when restricted to W, and that the inner product on V is uniquely determined by that on W and the dimension of N.

4. Let V be a finite-dimensional inner product space with matrix (a_{ij}) relative to a basis. Prove that the rank of $(a_{ij}) = \dim V - \dim(\text{radical of } V)$. (*Hint:* use the theorem that for a set of n linear homogeneous equations in n variables the dimension of the space of solutions is given by $n - (\text{rank of the coefficient matrix})$. (See §1-14 for a more conceptual discussion.)

5. Let V be a non-singular inner product space, W a finite-dimensional sub-space. Prove that W can be embedded in a non-singular finite-dimensional subspace. (*Hint:* if W is singular, pick $x \neq 0$ in its radical, and then y in V with $(x,y) \neq 0$. Show that in the subspace spanned by W and y the dimension of the radical has diminished by 1.)

6. Let V have basis $u_1, \cdots, u_n$ over K. Define an inner product by $(u_i,u_j) = 1$ for $i \neq j$, $(u_i,u_i) = a$. Let N be the radical. Prove that N is $(n-1)$-dimensional for $a = 1$, one-dimensional if $a = 1 - n$ and the characteristic does not divide n, 0 if $a \neq 1$ or $1 - n$. (*Hint:* the determinant

$$\begin{vmatrix} a & 1 & 1 & \cdots & 1 \\ 1 & a & 1 & \cdots & 1 \\ 1 & 1 & a & \cdots & 1 \\ \cdot & \cdot & \cdot & \cdot & \cdot \\ 1 & 1 & 1 & \cdots & a \end{vmatrix}$$

can be evaluated. Think of a as a variable. The first $n - 1$ derivatives vanish at $a = 1$ so we get a factor $(a - 1)^{n-1}$. The other factor can be shown to be $a + n - 1$.)

7. Let V have basis $u_1, \cdots, u_n$ over K. Define an inner product by $(u_i,u_i) = a$, $(u_i,u_{i+1}) = 1$, $(u_i,u_j) = 0$ otherwise. Discuss the radical for $n = 3$ and any a, and for $a = 2$ and any n. (*Hint:* the determinant

$$\begin{vmatrix} 2 & 1 & 0 & \cdots & 0 & 0 \\ 1 & 2 & 1 & \cdots & 0 & 0 \\ \cdot & \cdot & \cdot & \cdot & \cdot & \cdot \\ 0 & 0 & 0 & \cdots & 2 & 1 \\ 0 & 0 & 0 & \cdots & 1 & 2 \end{vmatrix}$$

can be evaluated. If we call it D_n, prove that $D_n = 2D_{n-1} - D_{n-2}$ by expanding along the first row, and deduce by induction $D_n = n + 1$. Conclude that the radical is one-dimensional if the characteristic divides $n + 1$, and is otherwise 0. For $n = 3$ and general a, the determinant is $a^3 - 2a$.)

1-2 The Direct Summand Theorem

The next idea we introduce is that of the orthogonal complement of a subspace. Let V be an inner product space, S any subspace of V. We define the *orthogonal complement* of S to be the set of all x in V satisfying $(x,S) = 0$, i.e., satisfying $(x,y) = 0$ for all y in S. Our notation for the orthogonal complement of S is S'.

Note that V', the orthogonal complement of all of V, is the radical of V.

As in the case of the radical, we leave to the reader the routine argument that S' is a subspace.

The phrase "orthogonal complement" probably suggests that S' may well behave as some sort of complement to S, that is, that the two subspaces S and S' are disjoint (or as disjoint as subspaces can be) and that S and S' together span V. We shall proceed to see that, under a mild and inevitable restriction, this is indeed the case.

First we need a basic remark. If V is an inner product space, and S is a subspace of V, then we may regard S as an inner product space by using the very same form (,). Note that even if V is non-singular, a subspace S may perfectly well be singular.

Note next that by definition, $S \cap S'$ is the radical of S. If we are to have $S \cap S' = 0$, as hinted above, it is indispensable to assume S non-singular. It turns out that for finite-dimensional S this assumption is sufficient.

Theorem 2. *Let V be an inner product space and let S be a finite-dimensional subspace that is non-singular relative to the induced inner product. Then V is the direct sum of S and its orthogonal complement S'.*

Proof. We have already remarked that $S \cap S' = 0$. It remains for us to prove that S and S' span V. Let x be an arbitrary element of V; we must express x as a sum of a vector in S and a vector orthogonal to S.

Pick a basis of S, say $u_1, \cdots, u_n$. To solve our problem we must find scalars $a_1, \cdots, a_n \in K$ and an element y in S' such that

(5)
$$x = a_1 u_1 + a_2 u_2 + \cdots + a_n u_n + y$$

Suppose $(u_i, u_j) = c_{ij}$. Apply to (5) the process of taking an inner product with u_i, $i = 1, \cdots, n$. Since $(y, u_i) = 0$, we find

(6)
$$c_{11}a_1 + c_{12}a_2 + \cdots + c_{1n}a_n = (x, u_1)$$
$$c_{21}a_1 + c_{22}a_2 + \cdots + c_{2n}a_n = (x, u_2)$$
$$\vdots$$
$$c_{n1}a_1 + c_{n2}a_2 + \cdots + c_{nn}a_n = (x, u_n)$$

We look at (6) as a system of n equations for the n unknowns $a_1, \ldots, a_n$. The matrix of coefficients, (c_{ij}), is non-singular by Theorem 1 and by our hypothesis that S is non-singular. Hence the equations (6) have a solution (indeed a unique solution), and Theorem 2 is proved.

EXERCISES

1. Let $\{S_i\}$ be subspaces of an inner product space V. Prove: $(\cup S_i)' = \cap S_i'$.
2. Let V be an n-dimensional non-singular inner product space, S an r-dimensional subspace. Prove that S' is $(n - r)$-dimensional.
3. Let x be a vector with $(x,x) = 0$ in a non-singular inner product space, and let S be the subspace spanned by x. Prove that S' has radical S.

1-3   Diagonalization

The process of diagonalization is normally thought of as referring to matrices. We shall indeed state the main theorem of this section in matrix form, but we prefer first to derive it in the inner product notation.

Given an inner product space V, we shall be seeking for it a basis u_1, u_2, $\cdots$ with the property that any two different u's are orthogonal: $(u_i,u_j) = 0$ for $i \neq j$. We call such a basis an *orthogonal basis*. If in addition we have $(u_i,u_i) = 1$ for all i, we speak of the u's as *orthonormal* and say they form an orthonormal basis. Orthonormality can usually be achieved only when the underlying field contains suitable square roots.

In the process of getting an orthogonal basis, characteristic 2 begins to create difficulties, as exemplified in the next theorem.

We make a definition at this point (*cf.* Ex. 3 in §1-2): a vector x is *null* (or *isotropic*) if $(x,x) = 0$; otherwise it is *non-null* (*non-isotropic*). We say that an inner product space is non-isotropic if it contains no null vectors.

Theorem 3. *Let V be an inner product space over a field of characteristic $\neq 2$. Assume that the inner product is not identically 0 on V. Then V contains a non-null vector.*

Proof. Assume the contrary, that $(x,x) = 0$ for all x. In view of the identity

$$(x + y, x + y) = (x,x) + (y,y) + 2(x,y)$$

it follows that $2(x,y) = 0$ for all x and y. For characteristic $\neq 2$ we get the contradiction $(x,y) = 0$ for all x and y.

Our discussion continues with the restriction, characteristic $\neq 2$. Later (§1-10) we shall devote a special section to the case of characteristic 2.

Theorem 4. *Let V be a finite-dimensional inner product space over a field of characteristic $\neq 2$. Then V possesses an orthogonal basis.*

Proof. If (,) is identically 0 any basis will do. Otherwise, by Theorem 3 there exists an element, say u_1, with $(u_1,u_1) \neq 0$. Let S denote the one-dimensional subspace of V spanned by u_1. Obviously the inner product restricted to S is non-singular. By Theorem 2, V is the direct sum of S and its orthogonal complement S'. If V is n-dimensional, S' is $(n-1)$-dimensional. By induction we may assume the theorem known for S'. Let $u_2, \cdots, u_n$ be a basis of the desired kind for S'. Together with u_1 these elements form an orthogonal basis for V.

Let $u_1, \cdots, u_n$ be an orthogonal basis for an inner product space V. Write $(u_i,u_i) = b_i$. Then the matrix of inner products is the diagonal matrix

$$\begin{pmatrix} b_1 & 0 & \cdots & 0 \\ 0 & b_2 & \cdots & 0 \\ & & \cdot & \\ & & & \cdot \\ & & & \cdot \\ 0 & 0 & \cdots & b_n \end{pmatrix}$$

Let $A = (a_{ij})$ be a given symmetric $n \times n$ matrix with entries in a field K of characteristic $\neq 2$. We can invent an inner product space V to go with it: we equip V with a basis $v_1, \cdots, v_n$, define (v_i,v_j) to be a_{ij} and extend the form to all of V by linearity. Now Theorem 4 asserts that there exists a second basis $u_1, \cdots, u_n$ with $(u_i,u_j) = 0$ for $i \neq j$. Say $(u_i,u_i) = b_i$, and let B denote the diagonal matrix with diagonal entries $b_1, \cdots, b_n$. Let P be the matrix effecting the change of basis from the v's to the u's, as in the discussion preceding Theorem 1. (Note that the roles of the u's and v's got interchanged.) Then we have $PAP' = B$. We summarize:

Theorem 5. *Let A be a symmetric matrix with entries in a field K of characteristic $\neq 2$. Then there exists a non-singular matrix P with entries in K such that PAP' is diagonal.*

The inevitable question that arises is: to what extent are the diagonal entries $b_1, \cdots, b_n$ unique? There is one easy, unqualified assertion that can be made (Ex. 1): the number of zeros is invariant.

On the other hand there are two superficial changes that can be made: the b's can be permuted (just perform the analogous permutation of the u's), and each can be multiplied by a non-zero square. (If we replace u_1 by cu_1, then $b_1 = (u_1,u_1)$ gets replaced by $(cu_1,cu_1) = c^2b_1$.) These remarks are merely the starting point of a profound theory, of which we shall indicate only the beginnings. The important point to be borne in mind is that the nature of the field K plays a controlling role. For instance, if every element in K is a square, then every non-zero b_i can be converted to 1. (In the notation above, replace u_i by cu_i where $c^2 = 1/b_i$.) We state this as a formal theorem, and note at once the matrix version.

Theorem 6. *Let K be a field of characteristic $\neq 2$ in which every element is a square. Let V be a finite-dimensional inner product space over K. Then there exists a basis $u_1, \cdots, u_n$ of V such that $(u_i, u_j) = 0$ for $i \neq j$ and each $(u_i, u_i) = 1$ or 0. If V is non-singular, each $(u_i, u_i) = 1$, i.e., V has an orthonormal basis.*

Theorem 7. *Let K be a field of characteristic $\neq 2$ in which every element is a square. Let A be a symmetric matrix over K. Then there exists a non-singular matrix P over K such that PAP' is diagonal with 1's and 0's on the diagonal. If A is non-singular, $PAP' = I$, the identity matrix.*

We introduce at this point the idea of equivalence of forms. If V and W are inner product spaces over the same field, and there exists a one-to-one linear transformation of V onto W preserving the inner product, we say that V and W are *equivalent*, and write $V \sim W$. In symbols: if f and g are the inner products on V and W, and T is the linear transformation, the requirement is $g(Tx, Ty) = f(x, y)$. We also speak of T as an *isometry* of V onto W.

If V is finite-dimensional and we diagonalize V with diagonal entries $(a_1, \cdots, a_n)$, we write $V \sim (a_1, \cdots, a_n)$. If a second diagonalization yields $(b_1, \cdots, b_n)$, we write $(a_1, \cdots, a_n) \sim (b_1, \cdots, b_n)$.

EXERCISES

1. Prove that the number of zero diagonal entries occurring in Theorem 4 or Theorem 5 is the dimension of the radical.

2. Return to the V of Ex. 6 in §1-1.
   (a) For $a = 1$, prove $V \sim (1, 0, \cdots, 0)$.
   (b) For $n = 2$ and $a = 0$, prove $V \sim (1, -1)$.
   (c) For $n = 2$ and $a \neq 0$, prove $V \sim (a, a(a^2 - 1))$.

3. Let $x_1, \cdots, x_n$ be elements of an inner product space V.
   (a) If the determinant of inner products (x_i, x_j) is non-zero, prove that $x_1, \cdots, x_n$ are linearly independent.
   (b) Is the converse true?
   (c) Prove the converse true if V is non-isotropic.

4. Let the inner product space V have an orthonormal basis $u_1, \cdots, u_n$. Let W be the subspace consisting of all $a_1 u_1 + \cdots + a_n u_n$ with $\Sigma \, a_i = 0$. Prove that W is non-singular if and only if the characteristic of the field does not divide n.

5. Let the inner product space V have an infinite orthonormal basis $\{u_i\}$. Let W be the subspace consisting of all elements having the sum of their coefficients 0. Prove that the orthogonal complement $W' = 0$, and that W is non-singular.

6. Return to the V of Ex. 7 in §1-1, and take $a = 2$. Let W be as in Ex. 4, but with n replaced by $n + 1$. Prove $V \sim W$. (*Hint:* use the basis $u_1 - u_2$, $-u_2 + u_3, u_3 - u_4, -u_4 + u_5, \cdots$ of W.)

7. Let K be any field of characteristic $\neq 2$ and $a \in K$. Prove $(1, 1) \sim (e, e)$ if and only if e is a sum of two squares.

8. Let K be any field of characteristic $\neq 2$ and $e \in K$. Prove $(1, 1, 1, 1) \sim (e, e, e, e)$ if and only if e is a sum of 4 squares. (*Hint:* the necessity is obvious. The sufficiency can be shown explicitly by a change of basis inspired by quaternions. Let $u_1, \cdots, u_4$ be an orthonormal basis. Say $e^2 = a^2 + b^2 + c^2 + d^2$. Take $v_1 = au_1 + bu_2 + cu_3 + du_4, v_2 = bu_1 - au_2 + du_3 - cu_4,$ $v_3 = -cu_1 + du_2 + au_3 - bu_4, v_4 = du_1 + cu_2 - bu_3 - au_4.$)

9. In Ex. 5 note that V and W are both non-singular but that $W + W' \neq V$. Thus observe that Theorem 2 requires the finite-dimensionality of S.

10. In the V of Ex. 6 in §1-1, assume $n = a^2 - a + 1$. Prove: $V \sim (1, a - 1, \cdots,$ $a - 1)$. (*Hint:* we have already done $a = 1$ (Ex. 2(a)). Assume $a \neq 1$. Take the diagonal inner product space with $(v_1, v_1) = 1$, $(v_i, v_i) = a - 1$ for $i = 2,$ $\cdots, n$. Set $u_i = v_1 + v_i$ $(i = 2, \cdots, n)$, $u_1 = (a - 1)^{-1}(v_2 + \cdots + v_n)$. Check $(u_i, u_j) = 1$ for $i \neq j$, $(u_i, u_i) = a$.)

11. (a) If the characteristic is 2, prove that the null vectors in an inner product space form a subspace.
    (b) Suppose given an inner product space with the property that the null vectors form a subspace. Prove that one of the following must be true:
       (i) any null vector is in the radical,
       (ii) the characteristic is 2. (*Hint:* if (i) is false take x null, $(x,y) \neq 0$, say $(x,y) = 1$. If $a = -(y,y)/2$, then $y + ax$ is null but $y + bx$ is not null if $b \neq -(y,y)/2$.)

1-4 The Inertia Theorem

A new circle of ideas arises when the base field K is ordered.

Definitions. Let V be an inner product space over an ordered field K. We say that V is *positive semi-definite* if $(x,x) \geqq 0$ for all x in V. We say that V is *positive definite* if $(x,x) > 0$ for every non-zero x in V. The definitions of negative semi-definite and negative definite are analogous.

Let K be ordered and let V be any finite-dimensional inner product space over K. Pick an orthogonal basis $u_1, \cdots, u_n$ (Theorem 4); let $(u_i, u_i) = b_i$. We can arrange the notation so that $b_1, \cdots, b_r$ are positive, $b_{r+1}, \cdots, b_s$ are negative, and $b_{s+1}, \cdots, b_n$ are 0. Let W_1, W_2 and W_3 be the subspaces of V spanned by these three batches of b's respectively. It is routine to see that the inner product restricted to W_1 is positive definite, to W_2 is negative definite, and to W_3 is identically 0. This proves the first part of Theorem 8.

Theorem 8. *Let V be a finite-dimensional inner product space over an ordered field K. Then V can be written as an orthogonal direct sum $V = W_1 \oplus W_2 \oplus W_3$, where the inner product is positive definite on W_1, negative definite on W_2, and identically 0 on W_3. In such a decomposition the dimensions of W_1, W_2, and W_3 are uniquely determined.*

Proof. We have already demonstrated the existence of the decomposition. The uniqueness of the dimension of W_3 is immediate; in fact W_3 itself is unique, since it is obviously the radical of the form (compare Ex. 1 in §1-3). The uniqueness of the dimensions of W_1 and W_2 can be handled expeditiously by inventing a suitable linear transformation. Let $X_1 \oplus X_2 \oplus X_3$ be a second orthogonal decomposition of V into portions that are (like the W's) positive definite, negative definite, and with inner product 0. Let T denote the projection of V onto W_1; the kernel of T is $W_2 \oplus W_3$. Consider T restricted to X_1; this is a linear transformation from X_1 into W_1 with kernel $(W_2 \oplus W_3) \cap X_1$. But the latter is 0; for if x is a non-zero vector lying in both X_1 and $W_2 \oplus W_3$ then $(x,x) > 0$ since X_1 is positive definite, and $(x,x) \leqq 0$ since $W_2 \oplus W_3$ is negative semi-definite. Now the existence of a one-to-one linear transformation from X_1 into W_1 shows dim $(X_1) \leqq$ dim (W_1). We get the reverse inequality symmetrically, and hence equality. The equality of the dimensions of W_2 and X_2 is entirely analogous, and Theorem 8 is proved.

Remark. This proof of the inertia theorem (the uniqueness of the dimensions) is valid verbatim in the infinite-dimensional case. But we cannot, in the uncountable case, assert the *existence* of such a decomposition. (See [32] p. 523, for an example that Savage attributes to Mackey.) For the countable case, see §1-15.

If we strengthen the hypothesis on K by assuming that every positive element is a square, in the above discussion we can convert all positive diagonal elements to 1's and all negative diagonal elements to -1's. Hence:

Theorem 9. *Let K be an ordered field in which every positive element is a* *square and let V be a finite-dimensional inner product space over K. Then we can find an orthogonal basis u_1, $\cdots$, u_n with each $(u_i, u_i) = 1, -1$, or 0. The number of terms that are 1, -1, or 0 does not depend on the choice of basis.*

We leave it to the reader to state the matrix versions of Theorems 8 and 9.

EXERCISE

Let K be an ordered field in which every positive element is a square. Let V be a non-isotropic inner product space over K. Prove: V is either positive definite or negative definite.

1-5 The Discriminant

Return to Equation (5) in §1-1, and take determinants. The result (after we note $|P'| = |P|$):

$$|B| = |P|^2 |A|$$

Thus the determinant of the matrix of inner products changes when the basis is changed. But if we grant that multiplication by a non-zero square in any case has to be absorbed (as it does in the diagonal entries after diagonalization), then we may speak of $|A|$ as an invariant of the form, and we call it the *discriminant*.

If one prefers, the ambiguity caused by multiplication by non-zero squares may be treated formally. Let K^* denote the multiplicative group of non-zero elements in the underlying field K, and write $(K^*)^2$ for its subgroup of squares. Then (for non-singular forms) the discriminant, and also the diagonal entries obtained after diagonalization, may be regarded as lying in the group $(K^*)/(K^*)^2$. Note that the discriminant is the product of the diagonal entries (in $(K^*)/(K^*)^2$, or up to a square).

The discriminant offers a way of computing the result of diagonalization, which is reasonably effective for hand work (at least up to 3×3 matrices!). We illustrate with two examples.

For the matrix

$$\begin{pmatrix} 2 & 1 \\ 1 & 3 \end{pmatrix}$$

the first basis vector could start the diagonalization, giving us the entry 2. Since the discriminant is 5, the remaining entry is $5/2$, or 10 if we prefer to avoid fractions.

For the matrix

$$\begin{pmatrix} 2 & 1 & -1 \\ 1 & 3 & 0 \\ -1 & 0 & -2 \end{pmatrix}$$

we use the already effected diagonalization of the subspace spanned by the first two basis vectors. To get the third entry, we compute the discriminant, -13, and then know that $-13/5$, or -65 if we prefer, is the required third number. (We are assuming characteristic $\neq 5$.) To summarize: the 3×3 matrix above is congruent to the diagonal matrix with entries 2, 10, -65.

A systematic statement of the method is as follows: given an $n \times n$ matrix A, call the determinant of the $i \times i$ upper-left corner the ith *leading minor* and denote it by d_i. Assume that A is symmetric and the d_i's are non-zero. (What happens if we encounter zeros is illustrated in Exs. 3, 4, and 5 of §1-8.) Then $d_1, d_2/d_1, d_3/d_2, \cdots, d_n/d_{n-1}$ are diagonal entries in a diagonalization of A.

Now let A be a symmetric matrix over an ordered field K. We say that A is positive definite if the form it determines is positive definite. This certainly implies that the discriminant is positive, i.e., the determinant of A is positive. The form restricted to any subspace is likewise positive definite. This is in particular true for the subspace spanned by the first i basis vectors. Thus we see that positive definiteness of A implies that all the leading minors are positive. The converse is also true: if in the notation above we have $d_1, \cdots, d_n$ all positive, then the diagonal entries $d_1, d_2/d_1, \cdots, d_n/d_{n-1}$ are positive. We state this as a formal theorem.

Theorem 10. A symmetric matrix over an ordered field is positive definite if and only if all the leading minors are positive.

EXERCISES

1. A symmetric matrix over an ordered field is called positive semi-definite if the form it determines is positive semi-definite. Prove: the leading minors in a positive semi-definite matrix are ≥ 0. Show that the converse is false. (*Hint:* try $\begin{pmatrix} 0 & 0 \\ 0 & -1 \end{pmatrix}$.)

2. To remedy the defective converse in Ex. 1 we introduce the *principal minors*, which are the determinants obtained by taking i rows and the same columns. (For instance, the 3×3 subdeterminant obtained from rows 3, 5, 8 and columns 3, 5, 8 is a principal minor.) Prove: if a symmetric matrix A over an ordered field has all its principal minors ≥ 0, then A is positive semi-definite. (*Hint:* if all diagonal elements are 0, then $A = 0$. Otherwise put a positive element in the upper left corner, sweep out the first row and column, and argue that the surviving $n - 1 \times n - 1$ matrix preserves the hypothesis.)

3. Let V be the inner product space of Ex. 7 in §1-1, with $a = 2$. Assume the field K to be ordered. Prove that V is positive definite.

4. Let V be the inner product space of Ex. 6 in §1-1. Assume $a \neq 1, 0, -1, -2, \cdots$, $-(n-1)$.
   Prove:

$$\frac{V}{a-1} \sim [a, a(a+1), (a+1)(a+2),$$
$$(a+2)(a+3), \cdots, (a+n-2)(a+n-1)]$$

$(V/(a-1)$ means V with the inner product $(x,y)/(a-1)$.)

1-6   Finite Fields

Thus far we have associated with a general symmetric bilinear form just one invariant: the discriminant. We ask, for which fields is this the only invariant that is needed?

Let us consider the two-dimensional case. Let a diagonalized form have (non-zero) diagonal entries a and b. Its discriminant is ab. A second diagonalized form with the same discriminant has entries 1 and ab. We require that there be a change of basis passing us from the first to the second.

In detail, if u_1, u_2 constitutes the first basis, we have $(u_1,u_1) = a$, $(u_2,u_2) = b$, $(u_1,u_2) = 0$. If v is to be the first basis element of the second basis, we have $(v,v) = 1$. Say $v = xu_1 + yu_2$. Then $ax^2 + by^2 = 1$ is the equation that must be solved for x,y in K. Clearly the procedure can be iterated with higher dimensional forms, and we obtain the following theorem.

Theorem 11. *Let K be a field of characteristic $\neq 2$ with the following property: for any non-zero a, b in K the equation $ax^2 + by^2 = 1$ has a solution for x, y in K. Let V be a non-singular finite-dimensional inner product space over K, and let d be its discriminant. Then we can find an orthogonal basis $u_1, \cdots, u_n$ for V with $(u_i,u_i) = 1$ for $i = 1, \cdots, n-1$ and $(u_n,u_n) = d$. Thus V is uniquely determined by the discriminant d.*

We next prove that finite fields satisfy the hypothesis used in Theorem 11. We prefer to abstract this in turn from two properties:

(1) -1 is a sum of squares, (2) the index $[K^*:(K^*)^2] \leqq 2$.

As regards (1) we obviously have

$$-1 = 1^2 + \cdots + 1^2 \quad (p - 1 \text{ summands})$$

in any field of characteristic p. What we are about to prove will incidentally show that -1 is a sum of two squares in any field of characteristic p.

For (2), let K be a finite field of characteristic $\neq 2$. The mapping $a \rightarrow a^2$ is a homomorphism of K^* into itself with kernel of order 2 (consisting of 1 and -1). Hence the image $(K^*)^2$ has order half that of K^*, and $[K^*:(K^*)^2] = 2$.

Remark. Statement (2) follows rapidly from the fact that K^* is cyclic, but we preferred to give the above direct argument rather than use this slightly deeper property.

Theorem 12. *Let K be a field of characteristic $\neq 2$. Assume that -1 is a sum of squares in K, and that the order of $K^*/(K^*)^2$ is 1 or 2. Then for any non-zero a,b in K, the equation $ax^2 + by^2 = 1$ is solvable in K.*

Proof. If $K^* = (K^*)^2$ the result is immediate, so we deal only with the case where $(K^*)^2$ has index 2.

From the fact that -1 is a sum of squares we deduce that any element c is a sum of squares:

$$4c = (1 + c)^2 + (-1)(1 - c)^2$$

Now it cannot be the case that the sum of two squares in K is always a square, for then every element would be a square, contradicting what we just assumed. Suppose $p^2 + q^2$ is not a square.

We turn to the solution of $ax^2 + by^2 = 1$. If either a or b is a square, the result is immediate. So we assume both are non-squares. It then follows from our hypothesis that a, b and $p^2 + q^2$ all lie in the same coset mod $(K^*)^2$. Say $b = r^2a$, $p^2 + q^2 = s^2a$. We take $x = p/as$, $y = q/ras$.

There are some infinite fields that satisfy the hypothesis of Theorem 12.

(1) K an infinite algebraic extension of a finite field. If a, b are any two elements of K they lie in a finite subfield of K. There we know that if a and b are both non-squares then ab is a square. From this we deduce that $[K^*:(K^*)^2] = 1$ or 2.

(2) Let k be any field of characteristic $\neq 2$ in which every element is a square. (For instance we may take k algebraically closed.) Let $K = k((u))$ be the field of formal power series over k in a variable u. (We may describe K as the set of series $\Sigma\, a_i u^i$ where $a_i \in K$, and the powers of u are integral, with only a finite number of negative powers allowed in each series.) In proving that $K^*/(K^*)^2$ has order 2, the crucial point is to show that a series of the form

$$1 + a_1 u + a_2 u^2 + \cdots$$

is a square in K. This can be quoted from the Hensel lemma of valuation theory, or we can justify the binomial expansion of $(1 + x)^{1/2}$, $x = a_1 u + a_2 u^2 + \cdots$.

(3) Example (2) can be generalized to suitable fields with valuations. One assumes that the residue class field has characteristic $\neq 2$ and is closed under square roots, and one imposes an assumption of completeness adequate to make the Hensel lemma hold.

(4) There exist still further examples of fields that satisfy the hypothesis of Theorem 11 (but not that of Theorem 12). Let k be an algebraically closed field of characteristic $\neq 2$ and K an algebraic function field in one variable over k; i.e., adjoin an indeterminate u to k and let K be an algebraic extension of $k(u)$. It can even be an infinite-dimensional algebraic extension, for the activity will take place in a finite extension anyway. Then the solvability of $ax^2 + by^2 = 1$ holds in K. This is moderately difficult to prove, and is part of a general theory asserting that suitable homogeneous polynomials have non-trivial zeros. See Lang [27].

(5) A final family of examples: take k real closed and K an algebraic function field in one variable over k, in which -1 is a sum of squares. (This time we really must take an algebraic extension of $k(u)$.) Again $ax^2 + by^2 = 1$ is solvable. The proof needs the result in (4) and additional arguments.

EXERCISES

Throughout these exercises characteristic $\neq 2$ is assumed. We introduce the following additional terminology: a form $(\ ,\ )$ *represents* $a \in K$ if there exists x with $(x,x) = a$. A form is *universal* if it represents every non-zero number.

1. Prove: every $(n + 1)$-dimensional form over K is isotropic if and only if every non-singular n-dimensional form is universal.

2. For a field satisfying the hypothesis of Theorem 12, prove that every non-singular two-dimensional form is universal.

3. Assume -1 a sum of squares in K and $[K^*:(K^*)^2] = n$ finite (note that n is a power of 2). Prove that every non-singular n-dimensional form over K is universal. (This theorem is due to M. Kneser and appeared first in *Math. Reviews*, Vol. 15(1954), p. 500.)

4. Prove: if every non-singular three-dimensional form is universal, then every non-singular two-dimensional form is universal.

1-7 Witt's Cancellation Theorem

We recall (compare the end of §1-3) that an isometry between two inner product spaces is a linear transformation that is one-to-one, onto, and preserves the inner product.

When we have an isometry of an inner product space V onto itself, it is customary to speak instead of an *orthogonal* linear transformation on V.

In the next theorem we show how reflection in a non-null vector gives rise to an orthogonal linear transformation.

Theorem 13. Let x be a non-null vector in an inner product space V. Let T be the linear transformation

$$Ty = -y + 2\frac{(y,x)}{(x,x)}x$$

Then T is an orthogonal linear transformation on V. It has the properties $Tx = x$, $T^2 = $ identity.

Proof. The final two statements are routine. Given y, $z \in V$ we have further to show $(Ty,Tz) = (y,z)$. This slightly longer computation we also leave to the reader.

In the initial version of Witt's cancellation theorem we build an orthogonal linear transformation linking two prescribed vectors.

Theorem 14. Let V be an inner product space over a field of characteristic $\neq 2$. Let y, z be vectors in V with $(y,y) = (z,z) \neq 0$. Then there exists an orthogonal linear transformation on V sending y into z.

Proof. It cannot be the case that both $y + z$ and $y - z$ are null vectors, for then

$$
\begin{aligned}
0 &= (y + z, y + z) + (y - z, y - z) \\
&= 2(y,y) + 2(z,z) \\
&= 4(y,y)
\end{aligned}
$$

a contradiction. Suppose that $x = y + z$ is non-null. We have $z = x - y$, hence

$$(z,z) = (x,x) - 2(x,y) + (y,y) \qquad \textit{law of cosines}$$

hence $(x,x) = 2(x,y)$. The reflection in x (Theorem 13) thus sends y into $-y + x = z$. If $y - z$ is non-null we similarly find that the reflection in $y - z$ sends y into $-z$. By following this with the orthogonal linear transformation that sends every vector in V into its negative, we get an orthogonal linear transformation that sends y into z.

We use the notation

$$(a_1, \cdots, a_n) \sim (b_1, \cdots, b_n)$$

for equivalence of diagonalized forms (see the end of §3) in stating Witt's cancellation theorem.

Theorem 15. *Over a field of characteristic $\neq 2$, suppose that*

$$(a_1, \cdots, a_r, b_1, \cdots, b_n) \sim (a_1, \cdots, a_r, c_1, \cdots, c_n)$$

with $a_1, \cdots, a_r \neq 0$. Then

$$(b_1, \cdots, b_n) \sim (c_1, \cdots, c_n)$$

Proof. By iteration we reduce to the case $r = 1$, and we simplify notation by replacing a_1 by a.

We take the point of view that we have two orthogonal bases of the same inner product space V. Say the first basis is $u, u_1, \cdots, u_n$ with $(u,u) = a$, $(u_i,u_i) = b_i$, and the second $v, v_1, \cdots, v_n$ with $(v,v) = a$, $(v_i,v_i) = c_i$. By Theorem 14 there exists an orthogonal linear transformation T carrying u into v. Necessarily T carries the orthogonal complement of u into the orthogonal complement of v, i.e. T carries the subspace spanned by the u_i's into the subspace spanned by the v_i's. This says

$$(b_1, \cdots, b_n) \sim (c_1, \cdots, c_n)$$

EXERCISE

Let a, b be elements of a field of characteristic $\neq 2$.
   Prove that

$$(1, 1, 1, 1) \sim (a, a, b, b)$$

if and only if a is a sum of 4 squares and ab a sum of 2 squares. (*Hint:* necessarily a must be a sum of 4 squares. If it is, then $(1, 1, 1, 1) \sim (a, a, a, a)$ by Ex. 8 in §1-3. Cancel: $(a, a) \sim (b, b)$, i.e. ab is a sum of 2 squares. The argument reverses.)

1-8   Hyperbolic Planes

Theorem 16. *Let V be a non-singular two-dimensional inner product space over a field of characteristic $\neq 2$, and assume that V contains a null vector. Then $V \sim (1, -1)$.*

Proof. Let u be the null vector. Complete u to a basis u, v of V. By the nonsingularity of V we have $(u,v) \neq 0$. We can normalize v so as to make $(u,v) = 1$. Suppose $(v, v) = a$. In this basis the matrix of inner products is

$$\begin{pmatrix} 0 & 1 \\ 1 & a \end{pmatrix}$$

and the discriminant is thus -1. If we take

$$x = \frac{1 - a}{2} u + v$$

we find $(x,x) = 1$. We complete x to an orthogonal basis x, y. Without any further computation we know by comparison of discriminants that $(y,y) = -1$ up to a square. Hence $V \sim (1, -1)$.

We call V a *hyperbolic plane* if it satisfies the hypothesis of Theorem 16, and we note that all hyperbolic planes are equivalent.

Theorem 17. *If a non-singular inner product space V (over a field of characteristic $\neq 2$ contains a null vector, then V contains a hyperbolic plane.*

Proof. Let u be the null vector. Since V is non-singular, there exists a vector v with $(u,v) = a \neq 0$. The subspace W spanned by u and v has as matrix of inner products

$$\begin{pmatrix} 0 & a \\ a & b \end{pmatrix}$$

and is non-singular. Thus W is a hyperbolic plane.

Now let V be a non-singular finite-dimensional inner product space over a field of characteristic $\neq 2$. If V contains a null vector then by the preceding two theorems (and Theorem 2) we have $V \sim (1,-1) \oplus W$. The process can be repeated on W and continued till we run out of null vectors. By Witt's cancellation theorem (Theorem 15) the end product is unique. We summarize:

Theorem 18. *Let V be a finite-dimensional non-singular inner product space over a field of characteristic $\neq 2$. Then V can be written as an orthogonal direct sum of hyperbolic planes and a non-isotropic subspace. The decomposition is unique up to equivalence.*

Theorem 18 means that the study of inner product spaces can for many purposes be reduced to the non-isotropic case.

EXERCISES

In all these exercises K has characteristic $\neq 2$.

1. Suppose a two-dimensional inner product space V has discriminant -1. Prove that V is a hyperbolic plane.

2. For any non-zero a, prove that $(a,-a) \sim (1,-1)$.

3. Let V be 3-dimensional with discriminant d, and suppose V has a null vector. Prove $V \sim (1,-1,-d)$.

4. Let V be non-singular and have leading minors $d_1, d_2, \cdots, d_{n-2}, 0, d_n$ with $d_{n-2} \neq 0$. Prove that $V \sim (W,1,-1)$, where W is the subspace spanned by the first $n - 2$ basis vectors, and that $-d_{n-2} d_n$ is a square. (*Hint:* Prove that the orthogonal complement of W is a hyperbolic plane.)

5. Complete Ex. 4 of §1-5 by diagonalizing when any of $a + 1$, $a + 2$, $\cdots$, $a + (n - 2)$ is 0 (but still $a \neq -1$ or $-(n - 1)$).

6. Let A be a non-singular symmetric matrix. Show that by a suitable permuta-

tion of the rows and columns of A (the same permutation for each) we can arrange that no two successive leading minors of A are 0.

7. Call the number of hyperbolic planes occurring in Theorem 18 the *index* of V. Call a space *totally isotropic* if all inner products are 0. Show that the index of V equals the dimension of any maximal totally isotropic subspace of V.

8. Let V be a non-singular $2n$-dimensional inner product space. Prove that V is a direct sum of n hyperbolic planes if and only if V can be written as the vector-space direct sum of two totally isotropic n-dimensional subspaces. (Thus the index is n, as defined in Ex. 7. One calls this a form of *maximal index*, and there is an analogous definition for odd dimension.)

9. Let K be an ordered field in which every positive element is a square. Prove the theorem of inertia (Theorem 8) for finite-dimensional inner product spaces over K by using hyperbolic planes and their cancellation.

10. If -1 is a sum of three squares in K, prove that -1 is a sum of two squares. (*Hint:* $(1, 1, 1) \sim (-1, W)$. Use Ex. 1 to see that W is a hyperbolic plane and then use cancellation.)

11. Let V and W be equivalent inner product spaces. Let f be an isometry of a finite-dimensional subspace V_1 of V onto a subspace W_1 of W. Prove that f can be extended to isometry of V onto W. (*Hint:* you can identify V and W. Use Ex. 5 of §1-1 to make V finite-dimensional. If V_1 is non-singular, cite Theorem 15. If V_1 has a radical, use techniques like Theorem 17.)

12. Prove that a hyperbolic plane has exactly two isotropic one-dimensional subspaces.

1-9   Alternate Forms

In the definition of a symmetric bilinear form, let us replace the hypothesis of symmetry by $(x,y) = -(y,x)$, which we call *skew-symmetry*.

Put $x = y$; then $2(x,x) = 0$. If the characteristic is not 2, we deduce $(x,x) = 0$. If the characteristic is 2, we cannot make this deduction, and indeed symmetry and skew-symmetry then collapse to the same thing. There is therefore some point in defining still another concept, calling a form *alternate* if (x,x) is always 0. Applying this to $(x + y, x + y) = 0$, we deduce skew-symmetry.

Summary: for characteristic $\neq 2$, "skew-symmetric" coincides with "alternate"; for characteristic 2, "skew-symmetric" coincides with "symmetric". This means that skew-symmetry is a superfluous concept. However its use lingers on deservedly, for in studying forms over a commutative ring the three properties are distinct. Indeed, skew-symmetric forms over the ring of integers have an important topological application [39].

Let V be a finite-dimensional vector space carrying an alternate form. Pick a basis $u_1, \cdots, u_n$, and let $(u_i,u_j) = a_{ij}$. We have $a_{ij} = -a_{ji}$ and $a_{ii} = 0$, and we take these as the defining conditions for an *alternate matrix A*.

Theorem 1, connecting non-singularity of V with that of A, goes through essentially unchanged, and so does the direct summand theorem, Theorem 2.

The arguments in Theorems 16 and 17 can also be repeated, even more simply, and without any characteristic restriction. We recapitulate: let V carry an alternate form which is not identically 0. Then we have vectors u, v with $(u,v) \neq 0$; we can arrange $(u,v) = 1$. The subspace W spanned by u and v has

$$\begin{pmatrix} 0 & 1 \\ -1 & 0 \end{pmatrix}$$

for its matrix of inner products, hence is a non-singular direct summand of V. Iteration of this procedure leads to the following result in the finite-dimensional non-singular case:

Theorem 19. *Let V be a finite-dimensional vector space over any field, and assume V carries a non-singular alternate form. Then V has a basis whose matrix of inner products is*

$$\begin{pmatrix} 0 & 1 & & & & & \\ -1 & 0 & & & & & \\ & & 0 & 1 & & & \\ & & -1 & 0 & & & \\ & & & & \cdot & & \\ & & & & & \cdot & \\ & & & & & & 0 & 1 \\ & & & & & & -1 & 0 \end{pmatrix}$$

Thus any two such spaces are isometric. In particular, the dimension of V is even.

We call a basis of the kind used in Theorem 19 *symplectic*.

EXERCISES

1. State the matrix version of Theorem 19.

2. Prove that the rank of an alternate matrix is even.

3. Let (,) be a bilinear form on a vector space. It is not assumed to be symmetric or skew-symmetric, but symmetry of orthogonality is assumed: $(x,y) = 0$ implies $(y,x) = 0$. Prove that the form is either symmetric or skew-symmetric.

4. Let V be a $(2n + 1)$-dimensional vector space on which we are given two alternate forms, f and g. Prove that there exists an $(n + 1)$-dimensional subspace of V on which both f and g are identically 0.

1-10   Characteristic 2: Symmetric Bilinear Forms

In the study of inner product spaces (symmetric bilinear forms) of characteristic 2, the first thing one misses is the possibility of diagonalization (Theorem 4). This trouble really exists; for instance, if the form is alternate there are no non-null vectors at all with which to begin a diagonalization. But it turns out that this is the only exception. The following theorem is due to Albert [1], p. 392, although over the field of two elements it was anticipated by Veblen and Franklin [36], p. 14.

Theorem 20. Let V be a finite-dimensional inner product space over a field of characteristic 2. Assume that V is non-alternate. Then V has an orthogonal basis.

Proof. We have a non-null vector u, and V is the orthogonal direct sum of the subspace spanned by u and its orthogonal complement W. If W is non-alternate we are finished, by induction on the dimension of V. So we assume W alternate. The discussion preceding Theorem 19 (or Theorem 19 itself, since it is harmless to assume W non-singular) makes it clear that the crucial case is where W is two-dimensional. In other words we may assume for V a basis u_1, u_2, u_3 with matrix of inner products

$$\begin{pmatrix} a & 0 & 0 \\ 0 & 0 & 1 \\ 0 & 1 & 0 \end{pmatrix}$$

and we have to show that there is a different basis, which is orthogonal. Let $v = u_1 + u_2 + u_3$. Then $(v,v) = a \neq 0$. We can finish the diagonalization begun by v, for the orthogonal complement of v is not alternate; for instance $u_1 + au_2$ is orthogonal to v, and $(u_1 + au_2, u_1 + au_2) = a \neq 0$.

We can push beyond mere diagonalization to a normalization of the diagonal elements by assuming (as we did in Theorems 6 and 7) that every element of the underlying field is a square. (Such a field of characteristic 2 is called *perfect*.) Actually it is natural here to make the weaker assumption that the form under scrutiny takes on only values that are squares: in symbols, $(x,x) \in K^2$. Or one can equivalently assume $(u_i,u_i) \in K^2$ for each element of a basis (the assumption is put in this form by Albert [1], p. 393).

Once this point of view has come up, it is natural to push on to a broader formulation. For any field K of characteristic 2, K^2 is a subfield, and K is a vector space over K^2. Furthermore, the set of values (say W) assumed by an inner product forms a subspace of this vector space. The case where V is alternate corresponds to $W = 0$. A slight extension of the remarks in the preceding paragraph can be formulated as follows: if V is finite-dimensional and non-singular, and the space of values, W, is a one-dimensional vector space over K^2, then V is uniquely determined by W. Indeed, if a is a non-zero element in W, then V has an orthogonal basis $u_1, \cdots, u_n$ with each $(u_i,u_i) = a$.

In Exercises 1 and 2 we explore what can be said when the dimension of W is 2 or more.

Witt's cancellation theorem (Theorem 15) fails in characteristic 2. Exercises 3 and 4 expand on this point.

For further developments see [26].

EXERCISES

1. Given V, an inner product space over a field K of characteristic 2, W the vector space over K^2 consisting of all (x,x), prove that V is determined up to equivalence by its discriminant and W if $\dim(W) \leq 2$.

2. In the same notation prove that V is determined by its discriminant and W, when V is three-dimensional.

3. By Exercises 1 or 2, or otherwise, prove

$$(a, b, b) \sim (a, c, c)$$

if a and b span the same space over K^2 as a and c.

4. For any non-zero a and b, prove

$$(a, a, a, b) \sim (a, b, b, b)$$

1-11   Witt's Theorem on Piecewise Equivalence

This second basic theorem due to Witt [43, Satz 7] can be said to reduce the theory of inner product spaces to the two-dimensional case, at least in a certain sense. We have inserted it here for its general interest, because it is used in [26], and because we shall prove and use an analogue of it in the next section.

Stated in terms of diagonalized forms, it asserts that when

$$(a_1, \cdots, a_n) \sim (b_1, \cdots, b_n)$$

we can pass from the first form to the second by a sequence of equivalences in each of which only two elements are changed. However, we prefer to state it in terms of a similar chain of orthogonal bases. To express the theorem briefly, we introduce the phrase "dyadic change" for a change from one basis to another of the following form: The first basis is, say, $u_1, \cdots, u_n$, and the new one uses $n - 2$ of the basis elements unchanged, replacing the remaining elements by two that span the same two-dimensional subspace.

> Theorem 21. *Let V be a finite dimensional non-singular inner product space over a field of characteristic $\neq 2$. Let $u_1, \cdots, u_n$ and $v_1, \cdots, v_n$ be orthogonal bases for V. Then there exists a chain of orthogonal bases, starting with the u's and finishing with the v's, such that each passage from a basis to the succeeding one is a dyadic change.*

Proof. We make an induction on n. Write $v_1 = c_1 u_1 + \cdots + c_r u_r$ where, after a change of notation, we can assume the c's to be non-zero. We make a secondary induction on r, the "length" of v_1 relative to the u's. If $r = 1$ then v_1 might as well be taken equal to u_1. Then the subspace spanned by $u_2, \cdots, u_n$ coincides with that spanned by $v_2, \cdots, v_n$ and we use our induction on n.

Suppose $r = 2$. Then the basis u_1, u_2, for the subspace W it spans can be dyadically replaced by $v_1 = c_1 u_1 + c_2 u_2$ and its orthogonal complement within W. This reduces our considerations to the case $r = 1$, which we have just disposed of.

Suppose $r > 2$. Write $(u_i,u_i) = a_i$. If every subsum of two elements of the sum

$$c_1^2 a_1 + c_2^2 a_2 + \cdots + c_r^2 a_r$$

vanishes, then every $c_i^2 a_i$ vanishes (this uses characteristic $\neq 2$), a contradiction. We may suppose $c_1^2 a_1 + c_2^2 a_2 \neq 0$. Write $w_1 = c_1 u_1 + c_2 u_2$. Then the basis $u_1, \cdots, u_n$ can again be replaced dyadically by the basis $w_1, w_2, u_3, \cdots, u_n$, where w_2 spans the orthogonal complement of w_1 within the subspace spanned by u_1, u_2. From $w_1, w_2, u_3, \cdots, u_n$ we can pass to $v_1, \cdots, v_n$ by our induction on r, since we have $v_1 = w_1 + c_3 u_3 + \cdots + c_r u_r$, an expression of length $r - 1$.

Theorem 21 fails for characteristic 2, as is indicated in Ex. 3. However the situation is different for the corollary of Theorem 21, which asserts that one can pass from a diagonalized form $(a_1, \cdots, a_n)$ to an equivalent form $(b_1, \cdots, b_n)$ by a chain in which two elements are changed at a time; by an additional argument this can be established for characteristic 2 as well (Ex. 4).

EXERCISES

1. Prove the invariance of the discriminant by using piecewise equivalence.

2. Use piecewise equivalence to give a fresh proof of the theorem of inertia.

3. Let u_1, u_2, u_3, u_4 be an orthonormal basis for an inner product space over the field of two elements. Observe that $u_2 + u_3 + u_4, u_1 + u_3 + u_4, u_1 + u_2 + u_4,$ $u_1 + u_2 + u_3$ is another orthonormal basis. Prove that there is no way of passing from the first basis to the second by dyadic changes. (*Hint:* no dyadic changes are possible at all!)

4. Prove the statement made in §1-11, that when

$$(a_1, \cdots, a_n) \sim (b_1, \cdots, b_n)$$

then even in characteristic 2 a chain of intermediate equivalences can be inserted, where at each step only two elements are changed. (*Hint:* follow the plan of Theorem 21. Trouble occurs if, in the notation above, every $c_i^2 a_i + c_j^2 a_j$ is 0. After disposing of some easy extreme cases, argue that all that needs to be done is to pass from (a, a, a, b) to (a, b, b, b) piecewise. For this construct an explicit chain.)

1-12   Characteristic 2: Quadratic Forms

The word "form" is merely a synonym for "homogeneous polynomial," and thus a quadratic form is a homogeneous polynomial of degree two. In two variables it is given by an expression $ax^2 + bxy + cy^2$. In n variables we may write $\Sigma\, a_{ij}x_ix_j$, but we must be careful. If we adopt the convention $a_{ij} = a_{ji}$, then for characteristic 2 all cross product terms will disappear. The usual procedure is to require $a_{ij} = a_{ji}$ for characteristic $\neq 2$, and restrict a_{ij} to $i \leq j$ for characteristic 2.

It is better still to formulate the matter in a coordinate-free way. Think of a vector space V equipped with a basis $u_1, \cdots, u_n$. Assign to a vector $x = x_1u_1 + \cdots + x_nu_n$ the number $Q(x) = \Sigma\, a_{ij}x_ix_j$ in the underlying field K. Then the function Q has the following properties:

(1) $Q(cx) = c^2x$ for all $c \in K$, $x \in V$.

(2) The function $(x,y) = Q(x + y) - Q(x) - Q(y)$ is bilinear in x and y.

If conversely we are handed such a function Q, and introduce a basis $u_1, \cdots, u_n$ in the vector space, then we find $Q(x)$ to be given by $\Sigma\, a_{ij}x_ix_j$, where $Q(u_i) = a_{ii}$, and $(u_i,u_j) = a_{ij}$.

We take (1) and (2) to be the defining properties for a *quadratic form*.

For characteristic $\neq 2$ it is plain that the notions of quadratic form and symmetric bilinear form are essentially identical; e.g. from the form (,) above we can recapture Q by $2Q(x) = (x,x)$. But for characteristic 2 we have a genuinely new gadget to study. Throughout the rest of this section (except in Theorem 25), characteristic 2 will be assumed.

In that case the form (,) introduced above is alternate, for $(x,x) = 2Q(x) = 0$. We shall study only the so-called non-defective case where this alternate form is non-singular. (Some observations on the defective case appear as exercises.) Note that the dimension of the vector space is consequently even; we write $2m$ for the dimension.

The first step in the analysis is to pick a symplectic basis (§1-9) for V, relative to the alternate form (,). We write $u_1, v_1, u_2, v_2, \cdots, u_m, v_m$ for a typical symplectic basis; we have that $(u_i,v_i) = 1$ for $i = 1, \cdots, m$ and all other inner products are 0. If we write V_i for the subspace spanned by u_i and v_i, then $V = V_1 \oplus \cdots \oplus V_m$, as a vector space decomposition that is orthogonal relative to (,). If z is a typical vector of V and z_i its component in V_i, then

$$Q(z) = Q(z_1) + \cdots + Q(z_m)$$

so that the direct sum decomposes Q as well in a natural way.

Let us take a close look at the two-dimensional case. We simplify notation by writing u, v for a symplectic basis of V (so that $(u,u) = (v,v) = 0$, $(u,v) = 1$). Write $Q(u) = a$, $Q(v) = b$. Then for a typical vector $z = xu + yv$ we compute that

$$(7) \qquad\qquad Q(z) = ax^2 + xy + by^2$$

a "concrete" representation of a two-dimensional quadratic form, normalized so that the cross-product has coefficient 1. We write $[a,b]$ as a shorthand for the form (7), and $\sim$ for equivalence as usual. The form $[0,0]$, i.e. xy, plays a special role and is written simply 0.

The expression $[a,b]$ enjoys a linearity property:

$$[a,b] \oplus [a,c] \sim 0 \oplus [a, b + c]$$

We prove this in a more general form.

Theorem 22. $[a,b] \oplus [c,d] \sim [a + c, d] \oplus [a, b + d]$

Proof. Let us set up the notation. We have a four-dimensional space V carrying a quadratic form Q, and a symplectic base u_1, v_1, u_2, v_2 relative to the alternate form attached to Q; $Q(u_1) = a$, $Q(v_1) = b$, $Q(u_2) = c$, $Q(v_2) = d$. We take a fresh symplectic basis, consisting of $u_1 + u_2$, v_2, u_1, $v_1 + v_2$. The theorem follows since $Q(u_1 + u_2) = a + c$, $Q(v_1 + v_2) = b + d$.

The next theorem is the analogue, in our present context, of the structure theorem on hyperbolic planes (Theorem 16).

Theorem 23. *Let Q be a non-defective quadratic form on a two-dimensional vector space over a field of characteristic 2. Suppose Q represents 0, i.e. there exists a non-zero vector u with $Q(u) = 0$. Then Q is equivalent to 0 (i.e. the form xy).*

Proof. We complete u to a provisional symplectic basis with v, so that $(u,v) = 1$. Say $Q(v) = a$. We then replace v by the better choice $v_1 = v + au$. Since $(u,v_1) = 1$, $Q(v_1) = 0$, the theorem is proved.

We examine the important special case where the underlying field is the field Z_2 of two elements. We have four possibilities in all for a non-defective two-dimensional quadratic form: xy, $x^2 + xy$, $xy + y^2$, and $x^2 + xy + y^2$. By Theorem 23, the second and third forms are equivalent to xy. There remain the forms xy and $x^2 + xy + y^2$, and these are distinct since the latter does not represent 0.

A general non-defective quadratic form over Z_2 is a direct sum of copies of xy and $x^2 + xy + y^2$. But by Theorem 22 the direct sum of two copies of $x^2 + xy + y^2$ can be replaced by the direct sum of two copies of xy. So the upshot is that we may have a direct sum of copies of xy, or the same augmented by one copy of $x^2 + xy + y^2$. That these two cases are distinct can be seen by a direct argument, or it follows from a cancellation theorem, which we shall prove in due course. But the best way to see it is to develop the theory of the Arf invariant.

The Arf invariant is the analogue, for quadratic forms of characteristic 2, of the discriminant. The underlying idea is one that occurs in many contexts: we replace the multiplicative structure of the field by its additive structure, and we replace x^2 by $x^2 + x$. In the light of this intention, let us formally introduce P for the additive group of all elements $x^2 + x$ in K, and write K_0 for the quotient group K/P.

Theorem 24. If $[a,b] \sim [c,d]$ then $ab \equiv cd \bmod P$, i.e. the images of ab and cd in K_0 coincide.

Proof. The notation is as follows: on the two-dimensional vector space V (over K of characteristic 2) we have the quadratic form Q and a symplectic base u, v with $Q(u) = a$, $Q(v) = b$. We are further given a second symplectic base s, t with $Q(s) = c$, $Q(t) = d$.

From the fact that $(u,v) = (s,t) = 1$, it is an easy deduction that the determinant of the matrix expressing s, t in terms of u, v is 1. For if $s = pu + qv$, $t = ru + sv$; then

$$(s,t) = (pu + qv, ru + sv) = ps + qr$$

The theorem is now easily proved by a direct computation. This direct computation (and the later one in this section for the general Arf invariant) can be replaced by more sophisticated, conceptual techniques. We prefer to keep the discussion on an elementary level, but let us avail ourselves of the resources of elementary linear algebra, such as the theorem that any matrix of determinant 1 is a product of elementary matrices. In this way we can confine our computation to the case $s = u + ev$, $t = v$, $e \in K$. Then $d = b$, $c = a + e^2b + e$ and $cd = ab + eb + e^2b^2 \equiv ab \pmod P$.

Theorem 24 justifies our calling the image of ab in K_0 the *Arf invariant* of $[a,b]$.

Let us complete at this point a discussion of non-defective two-dimensional quadratic forms over a perfect field K of characteristic 2. ("Perfect" means that $K = K^2$.) Say the form is $[a,b]$. If $a = 0$ the Arf invariant is 0, and we already know the form to be equivalent to the 0 form $[0,0]$. If $a \neq 0$, we can change the first basis element so that $a = 1$. Then one easily sees that the Arf invariant determines the equivalence class of the form. (Just reverse the small computation that occurred at the end of the proof of Theorem 24.)

Over a perfect field, the Arf invariant is all we need for non-defective forms of any dimension, but before we even know what this means we must develop the general Arf invariant.

We shall define it in a highly non-invariant fashion, and then pay the penalty by proving its invariance. Given a non-defective Q on V, we pick a symplectic basis $u_1, v_1, \cdots, u_n, v_n$. This decomposes V as $V_1 \oplus \cdots \oplus V_n$, and we define the Arf invariant on V as the sum of those on the V_i's. In detail: suppose $Q(u_i) = a_i$, $Q(v_i) = b_i$. In coordinate style the form is

$$a_1 x_1^2 + x_1 y_1 + b_1 y_1^2 + \cdots + a_n x_n^2 + x_n y_n + b_n y_n^2$$

The Arf invariant of Q is the image in K_0 of $a_1 b_1 + \cdots + a_n b_n$.

We shall prove the invariance by a head-on computation, but we begin by cutting the computation down to the four-dimensional case, using a theorem on piecewise equivalence, which has some independent interest.

As in §1-11, we use the phrase "dyadic change," even though this time four basis elements are changed. The theorem is valid for alternate forms in any characteristic, and we consequently treat it in that generality. Let then V be a finite-dimensional vector space carrying a non-singular alternate form (,); let $u_1, v_1, \cdots, u_n, v_n$ be a symplectic basis, so that $(u_i, v_i) = -(v_i, u_i) = 1$, $(i = 1, \cdots, n)$ and all other inner products are 0. Let V_i be the subspace spanned by u_i and v_i. By a *dyadic change* here we mean a switch to a different symplectic basis that changes two of the V_i's and leaves the others unaffected; that is, for a certain j and k, the elements u_j, v_j, u_k, v_k are to be replaced by another symplectic basis of $V_j \oplus V_k$, and all other u's and v's are left unchanged.

Theorem 25. Let V be a finite-dimensional vector space over an arbitrary field K. Suppose V carries a non-singular alternate form, and suppose given two symplectic bases of V. Then it is possible to pass from the first to the second by a sequence of dyadic changes.

Proof. We make an induction on n, where V has dimension $2n$.

Write $u_1, v_1, \cdots, u_n, v_n$ for the first symplectic basis. Let s, t be the first two members of the second symplectic basis. Write

$$s = s_1 + \cdots + s_n$$
$$t = t_1 + \cdots + t_n$$

for the decompositions of s, t relative to $V = V_1 \oplus \cdots \oplus V_n$, where V_i is the subspace spanned by u_i and v_i.

We first examine the case where for one of the pairs s_i, t_i (say s_n, t_n) both elements are 0. Let $W = V_1 + \cdots + V_{n-1}$. The elements s, t can be completed to a symplectic basis of W. We apply our inductive assumption to W. The result is a sequence of dyadic changes moving us from the symplectic basis $u_1, v_1, \cdots, u_n, v_n$ to a symplectic basis beginning with s, t. Passage from the latter to the given symplectic basis, which starts with s, t, is again possible by induction.

Next we note that since

$$1 = (s,t) = (s_1,t_1) + \cdots + (s_n,t_n)$$

at least one of the elements (s_i, t_i) must be non-zero. Thus we can suppose $(s_1, t_1) = a \neq 0$. Write $X = V_1 \oplus V_2$, $p = s_1 + s_2$, $q = t_1 + t_2$.

As a second case we treat the problem on the assumption $(p,q) \neq 0$, say $(p,q) = b$. The elements p, q/b can be used to start a fresh symplectic basis of X, and a dyadic change can be based on the passage from u_1, v_1, u_2, v_2 to this basis. This reduces the question to the case studied above, since $s = p + s_3 + \cdots + s_n$, $t = b(q/b) + t_3 + \cdots + t_n$.

Assume finally that $(p,q) = 0$. Then $(s_2, t_2) = -a$. We pass from u_1, v_1, u_2, v_2 to

$$s_1 + s_2, \; t_1/a, \; -s_2/a, \; t_1 + t_2$$

which is another symplectic basis of X. Again the problem is reduced to the first case, and this completes the proof of Theorem 25.

We turn to the invariance of the Arf invariant. By Theorem 25, we need only consider the four-dimensional case. But even here we prefer not to cope with a general change of basis, and use the discussion in Theorem 25 to reduce to two easily computed cases. Suppose given a symplectic basis u_1, v_1, u_2, v_2 with $Q(u_1) = a$, $Q(v_1) = b$, $Q(u_2) = c$, $Q(v_2) = d$. This gives us $ab + cd$ as a representative of the Arf invariant. Let s, t start a second symplectic basis, and write $s = s_1 + s_2$, $t = t_1 + t_2$ as above.

Case I. $(s_1,t_1) = 1$. We can absorb the change of basis from u_1, v_1 to s_1, t_1 by Theorem 24. We can suppose $s_2 \neq 0$ and then $(s_2,t_2) = 0$ implies that t_2 is a scalar multiple of s_2, say $t_2 = es_2$. Moreover u_2 can be replaced by s_2. The upshot is

$$s = u_1 + u_2 \qquad t = v_1 + eu_2$$

We can complete s, t to a symplectic basis in any way we wish (another use of Theorem 24), and we choose to use u_2, $eu_1 + v_1 + v_2$. We compute

$$Q(s) = a + c \qquad Q(t) = b + e^2c$$
$$Q(eu_1 + v_1 + v_2) = e^2a + e + b + d$$

The second version of the Arf invariant is thus

$$(a + c)(b + e^2c) + c(e^2a + e + b + d) = ab + cd + ce + c^2e^2$$
$$\equiv ab + cd \ (\mathrm{mod}\ P)$$

as required.

Case II. $(s_1,t_1) = f \neq 0, 1$. Then $(s_2,t_2) = 1 + f \neq 0, 1$. Thus s_1, t_1/f, s_2, $t_2/(1+f)$ is a symplectic basis. This again means that, after using Theorem 24 and making a change of notation, we may assume

$$s = u_1 + v_2 \qquad t = fv_1 + (1+f)v_2$$

We complete s, t to a symplectic basis by using

$$p = (1+f)u_1 + fu_2 \qquad q = v_1 + v_2$$

We have $Q(s) = a + c$, $Q(t) = f^2b + (1+f)^2d$, $Q(p) = (1+f)^2a + f^2c$, $Q(q) = b + d$. The changed Arf invariant this time is

$$(a + c)[f^2b + (1+f)^2d] + (b + d)[(1+f)^2a + f^2c]$$

and actually equals the original $ab + cd$.

We have proved a theorem, which we state laconically:

Theorem 26. *The Arf invariant is invariant.*

Note. This discussion differs from that of Arf [3] in minor details, especially the explicit introduction of piecewise equivalence. Klingenberg and Witt (*J. f. reine u. angew. Math.* 193 (1954), 121–22) have another elementary discussion of the Arf invariant. (I am indebted to Professor B. Huppert for calling this reference to my attention.) The paper by Kneser, which follows immediately (pp. 123–25) gives a more conceptual discussion by using Clifford algebras.

Now we can quickly treat the case of a perfect field. Each two-dimensional summand can be put in the form $[1,a_i]$. By iterated use of Theorem 22 we have that

$$[1,a_1] \oplus [1,a_2] \oplus \cdots \oplus [1,a_n]$$

is equivalent to

$$[1,\Sigma a_i] \oplus [0,0] \oplus \cdots \oplus [0,0]$$

Hence:

Theorem 27. *Over a perfect field of characteristic 2, two finite-dimensional non-defective quadratic forms are equivalent if and only if they have the same Arf invariant.*

The remaining important topic is the appropriate analogue of Witt's cancellation theorem. Since the proof we plan to give is actually valid over suitable rings, we defer it to §1-16.

EXERCISES

Characteristic 2 and finite-dimensionality are assumed.

1. Define the *radical* of a quadratic form Q on V to be the set of x with $Q(x) = 0$, $(x,V) = 0$, and define Q to be *non-singular* if the radical is 0. Show that the theory can be reduced to the non-singular case.

2. For any non-defective form Q, prove

$$Q \oplus Q \sim 0 \oplus 0 \oplus \cdots$$

3. Prove that the Arf invariant of $ax^2 + bxy + cy^2$ is ac/b^2.

4. Prove that for any non-defective form Q and any $a \neq 0$, Q and aQ have the same Arf invariant.

5. Call a quadratic form *diagonal* if the associated alternate form is 0. Prove that any quadratic form is the direct sum of a non-defective one and a diagonal one.

6. Describe all (not necessarily non-defective) quadratic forms over a perfect field.

7. Let K be a field with no separable quadratic extensions. Prove that any non-defective quadratic over K is equivalent to $0 \oplus 0 \oplus \cdots$.

8. (a) Prove that if Q is diagonal then the set of all $Q(x)$ is a vector space over K^2. Call this set the *range* of Q.
(b) Prove that a non-singular diagonal quadratic form is determined up to equivalence by its range.

1-13   Hermitian Forms

In this section we shall survey the high spots of an important broadening of the theory of symmetric bilinear forms. The main motivation comes from the case of the field of complex numbers, equipped with its operation of conjugation. The Hermitian forms that arise in this way have classical applications in analysis and geometry. The needs of algebra itself, as well as applications elsewhere, call for a formulation of adequate generality.

The whole chapter could have been developed from the start with the added generality, but for expository reasons we preferred to leave the Hermitian case to be treated at this point; it will in part serve the function of a review.

Our coefficients are now to be taken from a division ring D, i.e., an object satisfying all the axioms of a field except commutativity of multiplication. It is assumed that D is equipped with an *involution* *: an anti-automorphism whose square is the identity. In detail: $(a + b)^* = a^* + b^*$, $(ab)^* = b^*a^*$, $a^{**} = a$.

The (possible) non-commutativity of D forces us to make a choice between left and right vector spaces, and the decision is in favor of "left." Let then V be a left vector space over D. By a *Hermitian form* on V we mean a function (,) from $V \times V$ to D that is additive in each variable and in addition satisfies

$$(ax,y) = a(x,y) \qquad (x,ay) = (x,y)a^* \qquad (y,x) = (x,y)^*$$

If * is the identity (which forces D to be a field) the concept is identical with that of a symmetric bilinear form.

We divide the discussion of Hermitian forms into a number of subsections.

(a) *Dismissal of skew-Hermitian forms*   After the treatment of Hermitian forms has been completed, it might be expected that skew-Hermitian forms (satisfying $(y,x)^* = -(x,y)$) would be introduced to generalize skew-symmetric forms in the same way. However, nothing essentially new would be added. For suppose we are really in the new case where * is not the identity. Then from an element a with $a^* \neq a$ we get $b = a - a^*$ with $b^* = -b$, $b \neq 0$. Now given a skew-Hermitian form (,), we change both the involution and the form. Our new involution is $a \rightarrow \bar{a} = b^{-1}a^*b$, and the new form $f(x,y) = (x,y)b$ is Hermitian relative to the new involution. We leave it to the reader to check the routine details. For virtually all purposes, this device (taken from [20], p. 151, Ex. 4), makes it possible to replace skew-Hermitian forms by Hermitian ones. In sum: the two cases that need study are Hermitian and alternate forms.

(b) *Matrix interpretation*   Introduce a basis $u_1, \cdots, u_n$ in V. Given a Hermitian form (,), write $(u_i, u_j) = a_{ij}$. We have $a_{ij}^* = a_{ji}$, and the matrix (a_{ij}) is called *Hermitian*. Note in particular that $a_{ii}^* = a_{ii}$. Such an element of D is called *self-adjoint*, and we rephrase the observation by noting that all values (x,x) assumed by a Hermitian form are self-adjoint.

What happens to $A = (a_{ij})$ if the basis is changed? In a notation like that used in (4) page 3, we have $B = PAP^*$, where P^* is the conjugate-transpose of P, i.e., if $P = (p_{ij})$ then the i, j-element of P^* is p_{ji}^*.

(c) *The direct summand theorem*   Little needs to be changed in the proof of Theorem 2.

(d) *Diagonalization*   The one stumbling block is the need to produce non-null vectors. Let us note the implication of (x,x) always being 0. From the vanishing of $(x + y, x + y)$ we then get $(x,y) = -(y,x)$. Granted that the form is not identically 0, we can arrange x and y with $(x,y) = 1$. For any a in D we compute

$$a = a(x,y) = (ax,y) = -(y,ax)$$
$$= -(y,x)a^* = -a^*$$

Hence the characteristic must be 2 and * must be the identity. But in order to traverse genuinely new ground, we are assuming that * is not the identity.

We recall at this point that the diagonal entries obtained are self-adjoint elements of D. If a is one of them it can be harmlessly changed to bab^* for $b \neq 0$ in D.

(e) *The discriminant*   Only when D is commutative is there a useful determinant. In the commutative case we can take determinants in the equation $B = PAP^*$. So we are able to use $|A|$ as the definition of the discriminant, and it is invariant up to multiplication by a non-zero element bb^*.

Let us note at this point that when D is a field, the self-adjoint elements (i.e., elements invariant under *) form the fixed subfield K under *, and $[D:K] = 2$. The elements $bb*$ are the norms from D to K.

(f) *The inertia theorem* Without a close examination of the very best hypotheses, and the division rings that satisfy them, we assert briefly that the proof of Theorem 8 works if the self-adjoint elements of D are central and form an ordered field.

(g) *Finite fields* If D is finite it has to be commutative (by a famous theorem of Wedderburn).

Let K be the fixed field. It is a well-known theorem that every element of K is the norm of a suitable element of D. (Sketch of the proof: say K has q elements, and D has q^2. The multiplicative groups $D*$ and $K*$ have orders $q^2 - 1$ and $q - 1$. The involution * on D has the form $x \rightarrow x^q$. The norm homomorphism from D to K has as kernel the roots of $x^{q+1} = 1$, and thus the kernel has order $q + 1$. Hence the norm homomorphism must be onto).

In view of the fact noted above that diagonal elements can be changed by norms, we deduce:

Theorem 28. *Let V be a finite-dimensional vector space over a finite field. Then any non-singular genuinely Hermitian form on V admits an orthonormal basis; any two such forms are equivalent.*

(h) *Hyperbolic planes* Let V be two-dimensional and let x be a null vector in D. We can complete a basis with a vector y satisfying $(x,y) = 1$. The matrix of inner products has the form

$$(8) \qquad \begin{pmatrix} 0 & 1 \\ 1 & a \end{pmatrix}$$

where a is a self-adjoint element of D.

We call V a hyperbolic plane if there is some basis with matrix

$$(9) \qquad \begin{pmatrix} 0 & 1 \\ 1 & 0 \end{pmatrix}$$

If u, v is such a basis, then for the general element $bu + cv$ we have

$$(bu + cv, bu + cv) = bc* + cb* = bc* + (bc*)*$$

Let us call an element of D having the form $d + d*$ a *trace*. Then in order to be able to achieve the matrix (9) it is necessary that the form be what we shall call trace-valued, i.e., for all $z \in V$ we have (z,z) a trace. Conversely this assumption suffices. For assume that the element a in (8) can be written $a = d + d^*$. We replace y by $z + y - dx$. Then we still have $(x,z) = 1$ and now

$$(z,z) = (y - dx, y - dx) = a - d - d^* = 0$$

We remark that the trace-valued postulate is trivially fulfilled if D has characteristic $\neq 2$. It is also satisfied if $*$ is not the identity on the center of D. We leave this as an exercise.

(*i*) *Witt's cancellation theorem*   The argument in Theorem 14 does not generalize. The involution, non-commutativity, and the possibility of characteristic 2 all cause trouble; in particular we shall need the trace-valued assumption to cope with characteristic 2.

There is a "quick and dirty" matrix computation that can be used. (It is essentially due to Pall [30]; see also [23] and [20], pp. 162–5). Given y and z with $(y,y) = (z,z) = a \neq 0$ we have to find an isometry mapping y into z. This is the same as proving the equivalence of the form restricted to the orthogonal complements of y and z. Put in matrix form, we are given

$$M = \begin{pmatrix} a & 0 \\ 0 & B \end{pmatrix} \qquad N = \begin{pmatrix} a & 0 \\ 0 & C \end{pmatrix}$$

such that M and N are congruent, and we must prove B and C congruent. Here B and C are (let us say) $n \times n$ Hermitian matrices, and the 0's represent $1 \times n$ rows or columns of zero's. We do the computation in this block matrix style. Say $P^*MP = N$ where

$$P = \begin{pmatrix} w & X \\ Y & Z \end{pmatrix}$$

We get the equations

(10)
$$
\begin{aligned}
w^*aw + Y^*BY &= a \\
w^*aX + Y^*BZ &= 0 \\
X^*aw + Z^*BY &= 0 \\
X^*aX + Z^*BZ &= C
\end{aligned}
$$

We distinguish two cases.

(i) Characteristic $\neq 2$ or characteristic 2 and $w \neq 1$. In this case one of the two equations $\pm d = wd + 1$ can be solved for d in D.

Then by appropriate use of the equations (10) we get

(11) $(Z^* + X^*d^*Y^*)B(Z + YdX) = C$

(ii) Characteristic 2 and $w = 1$. Using the trace-valued hypothesis we can write $a = ad + d^*a$ for a suitable $d \in D$. Again (11) holds.

For a less computational proof, see [5], pp. 71–74.

EXERCISE

As in (h) above, prove the form trace-valued if $*$ is not the identity on the center of D.

1-14   Some Alternative Proofs

We reconsider the discussion that led up to Eq. (4) in §1-1. A reader might well feel that once the basic connection has been made between multiplication of linear transformations and multiplication of matrices, it should not be necessary to repeat a computation of this type. He would be right. The clue is to use dual spaces; because we preferred to avoid the use of dual spaces (possibly not taught in the reader's first course in linear algebra) we did not give the following proof at once.

Let us recall the context. We are given a vector space V with inner product (,) and a basis $u_1, \cdots, u_n$ of V. The inner products $(u_i,u_j) = a_{ij}$ give us the matrix $A = (a_{ij})$.

Now note that any element x of V gives rise to a linear function (a member of the dual space V^*) via the mapping $y \to (y,x)$. Let us write ϕ for the resulting linear transformation from V to V^*. Also, let $s_1, \cdots, s_n$ be the basis of V^* dual to $u_1, \cdots, u_n$. Then one readily verifies that A is the matrix of ϕ relative to the two bases $u_1, \cdots, u_n$ of V and $s_1, \cdots, s_n$ of V^*.

Let a second basis $v_1, \cdots, v_n$ of V be given, leading to the matrix $B = (b_{ij})$, $b_{ij} = (v_i,v_j)$. In §1-1 we wrote $v_i = \Sigma\, p_{ij}u_j$ and P for the matrix (p_{ij}).

Let $t_1, \cdots, t_n$ be the basis of V^* dual to $v_1, \cdots, v_n$. Then the matrix expressing the s's in terms of the t's is P'. Under these circumstances we know that the matrix of ϕ relative to the bases $v_1, \cdots, v_n$ of V and $t_1, \cdots, t_n$ of V^* is PAP'. Hence $PAP' = B$.

Next remark: the radical of the form is, by definition, the kernel of ϕ. Since we have just noted that the matrix A represents the linear transformation ϕ, this furnishes a proof of Theorem 1, which equates the non-singularity of A and of the form. Exercise 4, page 4, is also immediate.

Notice that if V is finite-dimensional and non-singular, ϕ is necessarily onto. This is the clue to a better understanding of Theorem 2. Recall that we had an inner product space V and a non-singular finite-dimensional subspace S, and our problem was to prove that V is spanned by S and its orthogonal complement S'. Take any x in V. By taking inner products with elements of S, x induces a linear function on S. We have just seen that this linear function can also be induced by an element s in S. Then $x = s + (x - s)$ is the desired decomposition of V into components in S and S'.

1-15   Infinite-Dimensional Inner Product Spaces

In this section we shall survey some aspects of the theory of infinite-dimensional forms, under three subheadings: diagonalization of countable forms, closed subspaces, and structure theory.

(a) *Diagonalization of forms of countable dimension*   We shall stick to the case of symmetric forms in characteristic $\neq 2$, leaving other cases to be explored in Exs. 1–3.

> Theorem 29. *Let V be a vector space of countable dimension over a field of characteristic $\neq 2$, and suppose V carries a symmetric bilinear form. Then V admits an orthogonal basis.*

Proof. It is harmless to assume the form non-singular. (If N is the radical, let Z be any vector space complement of N. Then the form restricted to Z is non-singular, and an orthogonal basis of Z, supplemented by an arbitrary basis of N, gives us an orthogonal basis of V.)

The proof now works in much the same way as the proof of Theorem 4; all that is needed is a supplementary precaution to make sure that the orthogonal basis being built up will finally span all of V. For this purpose we take a provisional basis of V, numbered off in a definite way: say $x_1, x_2, x_3, \cdots$. Moreover the x's need not be a basis; a spanning set will do as well. Suppose we have reached the following stage: we have $u_1, \cdots, u_k$, the first k elements of the hoped-for orthogonal basis. Thus $(u_i, u_i) \neq 0$ and $(u_i, u_j) = 0$ for $i \neq j$. Let S be the subspace spanned by $u_1, \cdots, u_k$. Then S is non-singular and hence (Theorem 2), V is the orthogonal direct sum of S and its orthogonal complement S'. Now let x_n be the *first* of the x's not lying in S. Write $x_n = y + z$ for the decomposition of x_n into components in S and S'. If z is non-null, it is our choice for u_{k+1}. If z is a null vector we can insert it in a non-singular two-dimensional subspace X of S' (for instance, a hyperbolic plane). We then take u_{k+1} and u_{k+2} to be an orthogonal basis of X.

The sequence of u's thus constructed forms the desired orthogonal basis of V.

(b) *Closed subspaces*   Theorem 29 is not true without the assumption of countability. We shall show this with the aid of the concept of closed subspaces and the closure of a subspace.

For any subspace S of an inner product space V, we take orthogonal complements twice, writing S' (as we have always done) for the orthogonal complement of S, and S'' for the orthogonal complement of S'. The following two properties are immediate:

(12) $S \subset T$ implies $S' \supset T'$

(13) $S \subset S''$

From (12) and (13) alone we can deduce $S' = S'''$, for $S' \subset S'''$ by (13) with S replaced by S'. Then apply (12) to the inclusion (13) to get the reverse inequality $S' \supset S'''$. Hence $S' = S'''$.

It is thus useless to take orthogonal complements more than twice.

We call S *closed* if $S = S''$, and describe S'' as the *closure* of S. Note that any orthogonal complement is closed. Note also that the radical of V is the closure of the subspace 0. As usual, there is virtually no loss in assuming V non-singular, for if there is a radical it enters harmlessly into all orthogonal complements.

The concept of closure plays no role in the finite-dimensional case, for if V is non-singular all finite-dimensional subspaces of V are closed. The following theorem gives a slightly stronger result.

Theorem 30. *Let V be any inner product space, S a closed subspace, T a subspace containing S such that T/S is finite-dimensional. Then T is closed.*

Proof. We can assume T/S is one-dimensional. Say T is spanned by S and x. Since S is closed and $x \notin S$ there exists $y \in S'$ with $(x,y) \neq 0$, and we can arrange $(x,y) = 1$. We claim that T' and y span S'. For suppose $z \in S'$ and $(z,x) = a$. Then $z - ay$ is orthogonal to x and S and hence to T. Thus $z - ay \in T'$. Now we proceed to prove that T is closed. Given $u \in T''$ we have to show that $u \in T$. Say $(u,y) = b$. Then $u - bx$

is orthogonal to both y and T', thus (as we have just seen) to S'; hence, since S is closed, $u - bx \in S$ and $u \in T$.

Our negative criterion for diagonalization is based on the next theorem.

Theorem 31. Let V be a non-singular inner product space that admits an orthogonal basis. Then the closure of any subspace of V having countable dimension is again a subspace of countable dimension.

Proof. Let $\{u_i\}$ be an orthogonal basis of V, i running over an index set, which has to be uncountable for the theorem to be interesting. Let S be a subspace spanned by a subset of the u's. Then S' is clearly the subspace spanned by the complementary set of u's. Thus $S = S''$ and S is closed.

Now if T is *any* subspace of countable dimension, then T is contained in an S of this kind spanned by a countable number of u's. (Express each basis element in term of the u's and collect all the u's that arise.) The closure of T is also contained in S, proving the theorem.

We shall apply Theorem 31 to the case of a real Hilbert space, assuming some modest knowledge on the part of the reader. We take the Hilbert space H to be separable (and of course infinite-dimensional) for simplicity. H is an inner product space over the field of real numbers. Take a Hilbert orthonormal basis $\{u_i\}$ of H. We must note carefully that $\{u_i\}$ is not an algebraic basis since it spans H only when infinite linear combinations are permitted. Indeed, the algebraic dimension of H is the power of the continuum. If S is the algebraic subspace spanned by the u_i's, the closure of S is H (in the topological sense as well as in the sense above). By Theorem 31, H cannot admit an orthogonal basis.

We shall present a variation on the theme, since it is of interest to have a similar example over the field of rational numbers, and since the example answers a question posed by Everett and Ryser [11]. We base the construction on a device from set theory. (Theorem 32 and generalizations of it can be found in many places in the literature. I learned this proof from P. Erdös; it appears in [24].)

Theorem 32. Let D be a countably infinite set. Then there exists a collection P of continuum-many subsets of D such that any two have a finite intersection.

Proof. We choose to think of D as the set of all rational numbers. For each irrational number α, pick a sequence of rational numbers converging to α. This gives us continuum-many infinite subsets of D. The intersection of any two is finite; for, given distinct irrational numbers α and β, the sequences approaching α and β ultimately lie in disjoint neighborhoods of α and β.

Now for the construction. We work within the sequential (real) Hilbert space of all sequences a_i with $\Sigma\, a_i^2 < \infty$. Let u_i denote the sequence with 1 in the ith place and 0's elsewhere. Let r_i be any sequence of positive rational numbers with $\Sigma\, r_i^2 = 1$. We apply Theorem 32 to the set of positive integers. For each of the continuum-many infinite subsets obtained, we construct a sequence v_α as follows: put the r's at the places corresponding to the subset (the order of the r's is unimportant) and put 0's in the complementary subset. The example V we want is the set of all (finite) rational linear combinations of the u's and v's. The inner product induced on V is rational-valued, for $(v_\alpha, u_i) = 0$ or one of the r's, $(v_\alpha, v_\alpha) = 1$, and (v_α, v_β) is rational for $\alpha \neq \beta$, since the sum involved is really just a finite sum of rational numbers. If we denote by S the subspace of V spanned by the u's, then (just as in the example of Hilbert space) the closure of S is V. On the other hand, the dimension of V is the continuum. Hence V admits no orthogonal basis. We note that V is a positive definite inner product space over the rational numbers, and thus furnishes an answer to the question asked by Everett and Ryser.

Suppose we require of an inner product space V that the closure of every subspace of countable dimension also have countable dimension. Does it then follow that V has an orthogonal basis? The answer is still "no." We conclude this section with a pertinent example, or rather family of examples, one for each field. The idea comes from an unpublished example that Donald Ornstein constructed for a different purpose in the late 1950's.

With K any field, we invent a vector space V over K with a basis $\{u_i\}$, i running over an uncountable index set. We are at liberty to define inner products at our pleasure, and we decree $(u_i, u_i) = 0$ and $(u_i, u_j) = 1$ for $i \neq j$. Take an infinite proper subset of the u's, spanning a subspace S. For ease of discussion, we write v's for these u's, and w's for the remaining u's. We wish to compute S'. Suppose

$$a_1 v_1 + \cdots + a_r v_r + b_1 w_1 + \cdots + b_s w_s$$

is in S', i.e. orthogonal to all v's. Taking inner product with v_1 we get

$$(14) \qquad a_2 + \cdots + a_r + b_1 + \cdots + b_s = 0$$

Taking inner product with a v_i different from $v_1, \cdots, v_r$, we get

$$(15) \qquad a_1 + \cdots + a_r + b_1 + \cdots + b_s = 0$$

From (14) and (15) we deduce $a_1 = 0$, and so $a_1, \cdots, a_r$ are all 0. Further, $b_1 + \cdots + b_s = 0$. The conclusion: S' is the set of all linear combinations of the w's with the property that the sum of the coefficients is 0. A very similar computation, which we leave to the reader, shows that the orthogonal complement of S' is S. Summary: S is closed, but is not a direct summand, for $S + S'$ falls one dimension short of V. Note in particular that the argument applies, with $S = V$, to show that V is non-singular.

Any subspace W of V of countable dimension can be embedded in a subspace S of countable dimension of the above type. It then follows (just as in the proof of Theorem 31) that the closure of W has countable dimension.

Our argument that V does not admit an orthogonal basis is based on a remark that is really valid for very general algebraic systems.

Theorem 33. *Let the vector space V have bases $\{s_i\}$ and $\{t_j\}$. Then there exist countable subsets of the s's and t's that span equal subspaces of V.*

Proof. Start with any s_i, write s_i as a linear combination of t's, write each of these as a linear combination of s's, and keep bouncing back and forth in this fashion ad infinitum. Collect all the s's and t's that arise this way. They span the desired subspace.

Return to the inner product space V described above, with its basis $\{u_i\}$. Suppose V has a diagonal basis $\{v_j\}$. By Theorem 33 there exists a subspace T of V having as a basis a countable subset of the u's or, at our pleasure, a countable subset of the v's. Looking at T in terms of its u-basis, we know (as shown above) that T is not a direct summand of V, i.e., T and its orthogonal complement do not span V. But since T also has as basis a subset of the v's, it obviously is a direct summand of V. Let us summarize what we have proved.

Theorem 34. *Let K be any field, V a vector space of uncountable dimension with basis $\{u_i\}$, and define an inner product on V by $(u_i, u_i) = 0$, $(u_i, u_j) = 1$ for $i \neq j$. Then V is non-singular, every subspace of V of countable dimension has a closure of countable dimension, and V does not admit an orthogonal basis.*

Remark 1. Theorem 34 is true as stated for any characteristic, including characteristic 2, but it is vacuous for characteristic 2 since the form is then alternate. (See Ex. 7.)

Remark 2. For a further variation on the theme of Theorem 34, see Ex. 6.

(c) *Structure theory*   Our point of departure in this subsection is the remark that there is no discriminant for infinite-dimensional forms, or at any rate there is no apparent way of defining one. What if the discriminant is the only finite-dimensional invariant, as is the case, for instance, for finite fields? The obvious presumption is that then nothing should be needed in the infinite-dimensional case; all forms should be equivalent. We shall prove this, and place the discussion in a natural, broader context.

Consider a non-singular inner product space V over a field of characteristic $\neq 2$. We proceed to extract hyperbolic planes for as long as possible. If the process terminates in a finite number of steps we might write symbolically $V \sim H_1 \oplus \cdots \oplus H_r \oplus W$, where the H_i are hyperbolic planes and W is non-isotropic. It follows from Ex. 11, page 21 that r and W are unique. We have nothing further to say about this case, which amounts to a reduction to non-isotropic forms. The case we shall pursue is the contrary one, where the hyperbolic summands go on forever. For a brief description let us then call V *infinitely hyperbolic*. If we throw in the assumption of countability, we get a decisive result.

Theorem 35. Let V be an infinitely hyperbolic inner product space of countable dimension over a field of characteristic $\neq 2$. Then V is a direct sum of hyperbolic planes.

Proof. The proof goes in two stages: first we get a direct summand that is an infinite direct sum of hyperbolic planes; then we arrange for this direct summand to devour its complement.

Take (Theorem 29) an orthogonal basis $\{u_i\}$ for V. For sufficiently large r the subspace spanned by $u_1, \cdots, u_r$ will contain a hyperbolic plane H_1. By the assumption of infinite hyperbolicity, there will exist a second index $s > r$ such that the subspace spanned by $u_{r+1}, \cdots, u_s$ contains a hyperbolic plane H_2. We continue indefinitely in this fashion; the resulting subspace $H_1 \oplus H_2 \oplus \cdots$ is a direct summand of V. Say $V = \Sigma H_i \oplus W$.

Write $-W$ for the inner product space obtained on W by replacing the form by its negative. Write H_∞ for a (countably) infinite direct sum of hyperbolic planes. By Ex. 2, page 20, we have $W \oplus -W \sim H_\infty$. We now perform the celebrated "Eilenberg trick." We have

$$(16) \quad W \oplus -W \oplus W \oplus -W \oplus \cdots \sim H_\infty \oplus H_\infty \oplus \cdots \sim H_\infty$$

But the left hand side of (16) can be regrouped as

$$W \oplus (-W \oplus W \oplus -W \oplus W \oplus \cdots) \sim W \oplus H_\infty$$

Hence $W \oplus H_\infty \sim H_\infty$. Since $V \sim W \oplus H_\infty$, we have $V \sim H_\infty$, as required.

Remark. This proof is somewhat simpler than the original discussion of these matters in [23], and is essentially contained in [14].

The next theorem records the natural hypothesis on K needed to put Theorem 35 to work.

Theorem 36. *Let K be a field of characteristic $\neq 2$ with the following property: there exists no infinite-dimensional non-isotropic inner product space over K. Then any inner product space V of countable dimension over K is a direct sum of hyperbolic planes.*

Proof. The extraction of hyperbolic planes from V must go on forever, for otherwise we would reach an infinite-dimensional non-isotropic complement. Thus V is infinitely hyperbolic, and Theorem 35 applies.

We note that Theorem 36 is applicable to any field K with the property that, for some fixed k, all k-dimensional forms represent 0; and we recall (Ex. 3, page 17) that this is true if $[K^*:(K^*)^2]$ is finite and -1 is a sum of squares.

EXERCISES

1. Let V be a vector space of countable dimension carrying a non-singular Hermitian form. Assume that either * is not the identity or that the characteristic $\neq 2$. Prove that V has an orthogonal basis.

2. Let V be a vector space of countable dimension carrying a non-singular alternate form. Prove that V has a symplectic basis, i.e. a basis $\{u_i, v_i\}, i = 1, 2, \cdots$ with $(u_i, v_i) = -(v_i, u_i) = 1$ and all other inner products 0.

3. (This is the only case not covered by Exs. 1 and 2.) Let V be a non-singular inner product space over a field of characteristic 2. Prove that one of the following holds: (a) V has an orthogonal basis, (b) $V = V_1 \oplus V_2$ with V_1 finite-dimensional and V_2 alternate. (For extensive further developments, see [13]).

4. Let V be a vector space of countable dimension over a field K of characteristic 2. Assume that V carries a non-degenerate quadratic form Q. Assume further that K is perfect or that K has no separable quadratic extensions. Prove that Q is a direct sum of copies of the form xy.

5. Let K be a field of characteristic $\neq 2$ for which the following is true: for a certain fixed integer k every k-dimensional non-singular inner product space over K represents 1 or -1 or both. Let V be a non-singular inner product

space of countable dimension over K. Prove that V has an orthogonal basis with diagonal entries ± 1. (*Remarks:* (1) The hypothesis is fulfilled by the field of rational numbers; the proof is decidedly non-trivial. (2) K has to be formally real for this exercise to be interesting; otherwise it is covered by Theorem 36. (3) When K is formally real, the theorem of inertia shows that the number of 1's and -1's is invariant.)

6. Modify the example in Theorem 34 by setting $(u_i, u_i) = 2$ instead of 0 and prove that the same conclusion holds. (This modification is of interest for it connects with a space having an orthonormal basis $\{v_i\}$: take the subspace of elements having sum of coefficients 0, and the basis $u_i = v_1 - v_i$ for it. Note that this shows the space spanned by the u's to be positive definite.)

7. Let the characteristic be 2 and define V as in Theorem 34. Prove that V does not have a symplectic basis.

1-16   Forms Over Rings

In this section we shall define symmetric bilinear forms and quadratic forms over commutative rings, and study diagonalization, the cancellation of hyperbolic planes, and a special result for two-dimensional forms.

For maximal efficiency the entire theory should have been developed from the beginning for an arbitrary commutative ring (or indeed an arbitrary—possibly non-commutative—ring with involution, so as to include Hermitian forms). For expository reasons, however, we think it is a sound decision to study the field case first.

Definition. Let R be any commutative ring and A an R-module. By a *symmetric bilinear form* (,) on A we mean a function $A \times A \to R$ that is linear in each variable and satisfies $(x,y) = (y,x)$. By a *quadratic form* on A we mean a function $Q: A \to R$ satisfying $Q(cx) = c^2 x$ for all $c \in R$, $x \in A$, and having the property that $Q(x + y) - Q(x) - Q(y)$ is bilinear in x and y.

If $\frac{1}{2} \in R$ (i.e., 2 is invertible in R) the distinction can be suppressed, but otherwise, just as for fields of characteristic 2, we have two distinct objects to study.

It is interesting to note that the classical concepts of proper and improper primitivity of forms have a natural formulation in this language; given a quadratic form Q on A and its associated bilinear form (,), we might require that $Q(A)$ or (A,A) generate the ring.

We discuss diagonalization only for valuation rings; greater generality than this seems impossible, or at least artificial.

Definition. A *valuation ring* R is a commutative ring with unit in which, for any a and b in R, either a divides b or b divides a.

The non-units (i.e. non-invertible elements) of a valuation ring R form an ideal that is necessarily the unique maximal ideal in R.

Theorems 37 and 38 are formulated only for symmetric bilinear forms. It would not add anything to insert quadratic forms, for orthogonal decomposition of a quadratic form is carried out by decomposing its attached bilinear form.

Theorem 37. Let R be a valuation ring containing $\frac{1}{2}$ and A a free finite-dimensional R-module carrying a symmetric bilinear form. Then A possesses an orthogonal basis.

Proof. Take a provisional basis $v_1, \cdots, v_n$ of A. Consider the elements (v_i,v_j), where i,j both run from 1 to n. There must be one of these that divides them all. If it is one of the diagonal inner products (v_i,v_i), the proof is ready to continue. Suppose it is (v_1,v_2) that divides all (v_i,v_j). In order to have a genuinely new case, we may suppose that (v_1,v_2) *properly* divides both (v_1,v_1) and (v_2,v_2). In view of the identity

$$(v_1 + v_2, v_1 + v_2) = (v_1,v_1) + (v_2,v_2) + 2(v_1,v_2)$$

and the hypothesis that R is a valuation ring in which 2 is invertible, we then get that $(v_1 + v_2, v_1 + v_2)$ is an associate of (v_1,v_2) and hence divides all (v_i,v_j). Now $v_1 + v_2$ can be taken as the first element of a new basis; for instance, we can complete a basis with $v_2, \cdots, v_n$. We have reduced to the first case and may thus uniformly assume that (v_1,v_1) divides all (v_i,v_j).

Write $(v_1,v_k) = a_k(v_1,v_1)$ for $k = 2, \cdots, n$. Let B be the submodule of A spanned by $v_k - a_k v_1$ ($k = 2, \cdots, n$). Then B is free on these basis elements, and A is the direct sum of Rv_1 and B, both in the module and inner product senses. The proof is now completed by induction.

Theorem 38. Let A be a free finite-dimensional module with a symmetric bilinear form over an arbitrary valuation ring. Then A is an orthogonal direct sum of free submodules, each of which is one- or two-dimensional.

Proof. We begin as in Theorem 37, picking a basis $v_1, \cdots, v_n$, and an element among the (v_i,v_j) that divides them all. If the latter is (v_1,v_1) we conclude as above. So the discussion continues with (v_1,v_2) again dividing all (v_i,v_j) and properly dividing (v_1,v_1) and (v_2,v_2). Write $(v_1,v_1) = e(v_1,v_2)$, $(v_2,v_2) = f(v_1,v_2)$. Then e,f are non-units in R and we shall use the consequence that $1 - ef$ is a unit. For $k = 3, \cdots, n$, write

$$(v_1,v_k) = c_k(v_1,v_2) \qquad (v_2,v_k) = d_k(v_1,v_2)$$

Then with

$$a_k = (1 - ef)^{-1}(d_k - fc_k)$$
$$b_k = (1 - ef)^{-1}(c_k - ed_k)$$

we have $v_k - a_k v_1 - b_k v_2$ orthogonal to v_1 and v_2. Let B be the submodule of A spanned by v_1 and v_2. Let C be the submodule of A spanned by $v_k - a_k v_1 - b_k v_2$ $(k = 3, \cdots, n)$. Then C is free on these basis elements, and A is the orthogonal direct sum of B and C. Induction completes the proof.

This is as far as we shall carry the structure theory of forms over rings. For rings that are not valuation rings, very little is known along the lines of structure theory, except for rings like the ring of integers, where it is a question of hard classical number theory. The situation is, however, more favorable for alternate forms. For instance, for alternate forms that are non-singular in the sense that the determinant is a unit, the usual canonical form can be established with a very mild hypothesis on the ring (Ex. 1). If the ring is a Bézout domain (all finitely-generated ideals principal), a canonical form of the elementary divisor type is available [22], p. 475, and some zero-divisors can also be allowed.

Before stating the next theorem we need some terminology. A commutative ring is usually called *local* if it has exactly one maximal ideal and is in addition Noetherian (i.e., satisfies the ascending chain condition on ideals). The Noetherian requirement is going to be irrelevant in what lies ahead. We shall use the term *quasi-local* to mean that there is precisely one maximal ideal, with no further requirements and in particular no chain conditions.

We introduce the term *hyperbolic plane* for quadratic forms over rings. Here R can be an arbitrary commutative ring and we are given a free two-dimensional module A supporting a quadratic form Q. We say A is hyperbolic if it has a basis u, v with $Q(u) = Q(v) = 0$. Thus Q on A is entirely determined by the value r of (u,v), where $(\ ,\ )$ is the bilinear form attached to Q. If r is a non-zero-divisor in R we shall call A a *non-degenerate* hyperbolic plane.

We now state our cancellation theorem for hyperbolic planes. In Theorem 39 the restriction to non-degenerate planes can in fact be waived. This requires fairly extensive further arguments, due to R. Wagner (Chicago thesis, 1968). The underlying idea of the proof is taken from the book of O'Meara [29].

Theorem 39. Let R be a quasi-local commutative ring, A an R-module *with a quadratic form Q. Suppose $A = B \oplus C$ and $A = D \oplus E$ are orthogonal decompositions of A with B and D equivalent non-degenerate hyperbolic planes. Then C and E are equivalent.*

Before beginning the proof we record an easy theorem concerning the behavior of the mappings induced by two direct sum decompositions.

Theorem 40. *Let R be any ring, A a (left) R-module, and $A = B \oplus C = D \oplus E$ two direct sum decompositions of A. Let f be the projection on B, restricted to D; let g be the projection on E, restricted to C. Then: if f is one-to-one, so is g; if f is onto, so is g.*

Proof. The statement that f is one-to-one simply says $C \cap D = 0$, and the statement that g is one-to-one says the same thing.

Suppose f is onto. To prove g onto we take $e \in E$. Write $e = b + c$ according to the decomposition $B \oplus C$. Since f is onto, there exists $d \in D$ with $f(d) = b$. Write the decomposition of d as $d = b + c$. Then $c - c_1 = -d + e$, so that $g(c - c_1) = e$ as required.

Proof of Theorem 39. We first carry out the proof under the assumption that B and D have an "overlapping basis vector." By this we mean that we can pick bases u, v for B and u, z for D with $Q(u) = Q(v) = Q(z) = 0$ and $(u,v) = (u,z) = r$. The decomposition of z relative to $B \oplus C$ may be written $z = \alpha u + \beta v + d$, where $\alpha, \beta \in R, d \in D$. Since $(u,u) = 2Q(u) = 0$, we compute $r = (z,u) = \beta r$, whence $(1 - \beta)r = 0$. Since $r \neq 0$ and the ring is quasi-local, β must be a unit. We now see that the projection of D on B, given by

$$u \to u$$
$$z \to \alpha u + \beta v$$

is one-to-one and onto. Hence (Theorem 40) the projection g of C on E is one-to-one and onto. Our remaining task is to prove that g preserves Q. We take $c \in C$ and write its decomposition in $D \oplus E$ as

(17) $$c = \gamma u + \delta z + e$$

so that $e = g(c)$. Now (c,u) and (e,u) are both 0. Hence on taking inner product in (17) with u, we get $\delta(z,u) = 0$, that is, $\delta r = 0$. Then

$$Q(c) = Q(\gamma u + \delta z) + Q(e)$$
$$= \gamma \delta r + Q(e) = Q(e)$$

(This first portion of the proof did not require r to be a non-zero-divisor, but merely that it be non-zero.)

We continue the proof, dropping the assumption of an overlapping basis vector. Our notation for bases will now be u, v for B and y, z for D. We have $Q(u) = Q(v) = Q(y) = Q(z) = 0$ and $(u,v) = (y,z) = r$.

We note that (u,A) consists of multiples of r, and in particular (u,y) is a multiple of r. We distinguish two cases.

(a) (u,y) is a unit multiple of r, say $(u,y) = \epsilon r$. Since we can harmlessly replace y by $\epsilon^{-1}y$ and z by ϵz, we can even assume $(u,y) = r$.

The idea we use is to show that the submodule H spanned by u and y is a hyperbolic plane, and that A is the direct sum of H and its orthogonal complement J. For then we can move from $B \oplus C$ to $D \oplus E$ by two applications of the first part of the proof; that is, we have $C \sim J$ because B and H have an overlapping vector, $J \sim E$ because H and D have an overlapping vector, and hence $C \sim E$.

First we dispose of the question of the linear independence of u and y. If $\rho u + \sigma y = 0$, $(\rho, \sigma \in R)$, then by taking inner product with u we get $\sigma r = 0$, whence $\sigma = 0$ since r is a non-zero-divisor. Similarly $\rho = 0$. This proves u and y to be linearly independent, so that they form a free basis of H. Moreover, the same argument shows that $H \cap J = 0$. To show that $H \oplus J$ spans A, we begin by noting $(H,A) \subset rR$. For any x in A we therefore have that (x,u) and (x,y) are multiples of r, say $(x,u) = \lambda r$, $(x,y) = \mu r$. The equation

$$x = \mu u + \lambda y + (x - \mu u - \lambda y)$$

gives us an expression of x as the sum of an element in H and an element in J. This concludes the discussion of case (a).

(b) In this remaining case we may assume that (u,y), (u,z), (v,y), and (v,z) are all proper multiples of r. Then $(u, v + y)$ is a unit times r. This puts us in a position to use the submodule H_0 spanned by u and $v_0 = v + y$. It is a hyperbolic plane just as in part (a), and A is an orthogonal direct sum of H_0 and its orthogonal complement J_0. The bases u, v and u, v_0 overlap; thus we get $C \sim J_0$ from the first part of the proof. Since (z,v_0) also has the form (unit)r, the passage from u, v_0 to y, z is covered by case (a), and thus $J_0 \sim E$. Hence $C \sim E$, and the proof of Theorem 39 is finished.

We record two consequences of Theorem 39. Each is based on the following idea: by iteration of Theorem 39 we can cancel a direct sum of non-degenerate hyperbolic planes. Moreover, we can cancel a direct summand of a direct sum of non-degenerate hyperbolic planes. In detail:

suppose that $B \oplus D \sim B \oplus E$, that $A = B \oplus C$, and that A is a direct sum of non-degenerate hyperbolic planes. We add C to each side, getting

$$C \oplus B \oplus D \sim C \oplus B \oplus E$$

i.e., $A \oplus D \sim A \oplus E$, and then we cancel A.

Let R be a commutative ring that need not be quasi-local; assume $\frac{1}{2} \in R$. Consider a quadratic form Q on a one-dimensional free module B. Say B is generated by u, and $Q(u) = a$. We invent a module which we call $-B$; it is free on a generator v, and we set $Q(v) = -a$. Then $B \oplus -B$ is a hyperbolic plane, as the basis $u + v$, $u - v$ shows. The inner product $(u + v, u - v)$ is $4a$. We deduce:

Theorem 41. *Let R be a quasi-local commutative ring containing $\frac{1}{2}$. Let A, B, and C be R-modules carrying quadratic forms (it would be equivalent to say symmetric bilinear forms). Assume that A is free, finite-dimensional, and possesses an orthogonal basis with diagonal elements that are non-zero divisors. Then $A \oplus B \sim A \oplus C$ implies $B \sim C$.*

The next theorem is in a similar way a consequence of Theorem 39 and Ex. 2, page 33.

Theorem 42. *Over a field of characteristic 2, let V, W, and X be vector spaces carrying quadratic forms. Assume that V is finite-dimensional, and that its quadratic form is non-defective. Then $V \oplus W \sim V \oplus X$ implies $W \sim X$.*

Our final topic in this section comes from some of the most venerable work in number theory. In the ring of integers, the primes that can be written as sums of two squares are exactly those of the form $4n + 1$; this is true number theory and is not on our agenda (but see Exs. 7–9 for what we might call a start on the ring theory of binary quadratic forms). A companion theorem asserts that the representation is essentially unique; this can be regarded as an instance of a general algebraic theorem. Our point of view will be to show that such a representation is unique up to an automorphism of the underlying quadratic form. Completion of the problem above then requires the knowledge that, over the ring of integers, the form $x^2 + y^2$ admits only trivial automorphisms.

We actually shall prove two theorems, the first dealing with the uniqueness of the representation of a unit.

Theorem 43. *Let R be any commutative ring, A a free two-dimensional R-module carrying a quadratic form Q. Let u and w be elements of A with Q(u) = Q(w) = a unit a of R. Then there exists an isometry of A onto itself that carries u into w.*

Remark. If $\frac{1}{2} \in R$, then u and w span direct summands of A and we can easily prove Theorem 43 by a comparison of discriminants.

Proof. Since $Q(u) =$ a unit, we can pick u to be a basis element of A. In detail: take a provisional basis of A, say s and t. In terms of this basis, say the quadratic form is $Q(xs + yt) = px^2 + qxy + ry^2$. Then if $u = x_0 s + y_0 t$, we have $px_0^2 + qx_0 y_0 + ry_0^2 = a$, a unit. Hence the ideal generated by x_0 and y_0 is the whole ring R. It follows that we can change basis from s, t to u and a suitable second element v.

In terms of u, v let Q be $ax^2 + bxy + cy^2$. Say $w = mu + nv$, so that $a = Q(w) = am^2 + bmn + cn^2$. Define z by

$$az = -cnu + (am + bn)v$$

Then the determinant of w, z relative to u, v is 1, $(w,z) = b$ and $Q(z) = c$. These statements are proved by direct brutal verification, which the reader should carry out; it is not suitable for the printed page. In making the computation one should note $(u,u) = 2Q(u) = 2a$, $(u,v) = b$, $(v,v) = 2Q(v) = 2c$.

With all this verified, we are able to define an isometry of A upon itself by sending u into w and v into z.

Our final theorem needs some modest restrictions on the ring and on the element represented.

Theorem 44. *Let R be an integral domain (commutative ring with unit and no zero-divisors), and let A be a free two-dimensional R-module carrying a quadratic form Q. Let u and w be elements of A such that Q(u) = Q(w) = an element π generating a maximal ideal of R. Then there exists an isometry of A onto itself that carries u into w.*

Proof. Again we begin by showing that u can be a basis element of A. We use the same notation as in the beginning of the proof of Theorem 43. This time we reach $px_0^2 + qx_0 y_0 + ry_0^2 = \pi$. Let J be the ideal generated by x_0 and y_0. We wish to prove $J = R$, and we suppose the contrary. We have $\pi \in J^2$. Since (π) is by hypothesis a maximal ideal, this entails $(\pi) = J^2$, which leads to $(\pi) = J$, an impossibility since it makes π divisible by π^2.

We take u, v as our basis for A, $\pi x^2 + bxy + cy^2$ as the quadratic form, and $w = mu + nv$. Thus

(18) $$\pi m^2 + bmn + cn^2 = \pi$$

It follows that π divides $bmn + cn^2 = n(bm + cn)$, and π must divide one of the factors. We distinguish two cases.

I. π divides n. Write $n = \pi n_0$. From (18), and the assumption that R is a domain, we get

(19) $$m^2 + bmn_0 + cnn_0 = 1$$

Set $z = -cn_0u + (m + bn_0)v$. Equation (19) tells us that the determinant of w, z relative to u, v is 1. More brutal verification establishes $(w,t) = b$ and $Q(z) = c$.

II. π divides $bm + cn$. Write

(20) $$bm + cn = d\pi$$

Now (18) and (20) yield

(21) $$m^2 + dn = 1$$

Take $z = du - mv$. This time the determinant of w, z relative to u, v is -1 by (21). The verification of $(w,z) = b$ and $Q(z) = c$ is a little less routine and we give the details.

$$(w,z) = 2md\pi + b(dn - m^2) - 2mnc$$
$$= 2m(bm + cn) + b(2dn - 1) - 2mnc$$

by (20) and (21). This simplifies to

$$(w,z) = 2b(m^2 + dn) - b$$

which equals b by another application of (21).

$$Q(z) = d^2\pi - dmb + m^2c$$
$$= d(bm + cn) - dmb + m^2c$$
$$= dcn + m^2c = c(dn + m^2) = c$$

by (20) and (21).

In both cases, sending u into w and v into z is an isometry of A onto itself. We have completed the proof of Theorem 44.

Remark. It is worth noting that the isometry we constructed had determinant 1 in Theorem 43 and Case I of Theorem 44, determinant -1 in Case II of Theorem 44.

There is another proof of Theorem 44 that requires more elaborate computations, but yields a stronger result. See Ex. 11.

EXERCISES

1. Let R be any commutative ring with unit, and A a free finite-dimensional R-module carrying an alternate form whose determinant is a unit. Assume that R has the following property: if a projective module P satisfies $P \oplus F_1 = F_2$, where F_1 and F_2 are finite-dimensional free, then P is free. Prove that A has a symplectic basis. (*Hint:* the form induces an isomorphism of A onto its dual A^*. Take a provisional basis $u_1, \cdots, u_n$ of A and the dual basis $w_1, \cdots, w_n$ of A^*. If $v_1 \in A$ corresponds to w_1, we have $(u_1, v_1) = 1$. Argue a la Theorem 2 that u_1 and v_1 span an orthogonal direct summand of A. Use the hypothesis to make sure that the complement is free).

2. Let R be a Bézout domain. Let A be a free finite-dimensional R-module carrying a symmetric bilinear form whose determinant is a unit. Assume that the form represents 0. Prove that A has a free two-dimensional orthogonal direct summand. (*Hint:* $(u, u) = 0$ with $u \neq 0$. We can arrange, by dividing by a scalar if necessary, that u can serve as a basis element. Treat it as u_1 was treated in Ex. 1. Note that if $\frac{1}{2} \in R$ we get a hyperbolic plane.)

   Let us use the classical term *binary quadratic form* for the object studied in Theorems 43 and 44: a quadratic form on a two-dimensional free module over a commutative ring. In coordinate style we get $ax^2 + bxy + cy^2$. Over a Bézout domain we call the form *primitive* if the greatest common divisor of a, b, c is 1.

3. Let Q be a primitive binary quadratic form over a Bézout domain R. Suppose Q represents 0 but is non-degenerate in the sense that its discriminant is non-zero. Show that Q can be put in the form $bx^2 + cy^2$, and that a complete set of invariants is given by b (up to a unit factor) and the class of c mod b, provided c is identified with its inverse mod b. (*Hint:* take an adjusted null vector as first basis vector; to change c and b change the second basis vector by a multiple of the first; to switch to the inverse of c mod b locate a second null vector. Compare [21], p. 173.)

4. (This simple-minded exercise illustrates the failure of Theorem 44 where π is not a prime. Exercises 5 and 6 are illustrations of failure for dimension

greater than two). Over the ring of integers the form $x^2 + y^2$ represents 65 via the vectors $(8, 1)$ and $(7, 4)$; prove that these vectors are not equivalent under an isometry of the form.

5. Over the ring of integers
   (a) the form $x^2 + yz$ represents 1 via $(1, 0, 0)$ and $(1, -1, 0)$,
   (b) the form $x^2 + 2y^2 + 3z^2$ represents 3 via $(1, 1, 0)$ and $(0, 0, 1)$.

   Prove that in both cases the vectors are not equivalent under an isometry of the form. (These examples come from [21], pp. 102–3. The non-equivalence still holds when the ring is extended to the 2-adic and 3-adic integers respectively.)

6. (a) Prove that over an arbitrary commutative ring the quadratic forms $x^2 + y^2 - z^2$ and $x^2 - 2yz$ are equivalent. (Set $x = u + v$, $y = u + w$, $z = u + v + w$ to pass from the first to the second.)
   (b) Prove that the quadratic forms $2xy$ and $x^2 - y^2$ are equivalent over a commutative ring R if and only if $\frac{1}{2} \in R$.

7. This exercise and the succeeding one concern isometries of a binary quadratic form over an integral domain R, called *automorphs* in the literature of number theory. Such an automorph must have determinant ± 1. We assume characteristic $\neq 2$; the reader is invited to explore the case of characteristic 2. The notation I^{-1} is the inverse used in ideal theory, the set of all x in the quotient field of R satisfying $xI \subset R$.

   Notation: u, v a basis for a free module A, $Q(u) = a$, $Q(v) = c$, $(u,v) = b$. F is a map from A onto itself by $F(u) = pu + qv$, $F(v) = ru + sv$. In this exercise assume $ps - qr = 1$. Prove that F preserves Q if and only if

   $$q = ta, \quad r = -tc, \quad s = q + tb, \quad t \in (a, b, c)^{-1}$$

   where p and t satisfy the "Pell equation"

   $$p^2 + bpt + act^2 = 1$$

8. Let Q be a binary quadratic form over a Bézout domain of characteristic $\neq 2$. Show that Q admits an isometry of determinant -1 if and only if, in a suitable basis, $Q = ax^2 + bxy + cy^2$ with b a multiple of a. (This result goes back to Gauss. He called such forms *ambiguous*.)

9. In this exercise R is any commutative ring, $Q = ax^2 + bxy + cy^2$ is a binary quadratic form over R. If $au^2 + buv + cv^2 = m$ for suitable u and v, we say that Q represents m. If the ideal $(u, v) = R$, we call the representation *primitive*. The discriminant Δ is $4ac - b^2$.
   (a) If Q represents m, prove that $4am$ is a square mod Δ. (*Hint*: complete the square, $4am = (2ax + by)^2 + \Delta y^2$.)
   (b) If Q primitively represents m, prove that $-\Delta$ is a square mod $4m$. (*Hint*: the vector representing m can be the first basis vector. Then the form is $mx^2 + pxy + qy^2$, and $\Delta = 4mq - p^2$.)

(c) Conversely if $-\Delta$ is a square mod $4m$, prove that m is primitively represented by *some* form of discriminant Δ. (*Hint:* if $-\Delta = u^2 - 4km$, take the form $mx^2 + uxy + ky^2$.)

(d) If $Q = ax^2 + 2bxy + cy^2$, it is natural to define the *reduced discriminant* $\Delta_0 = ac - b^2$. Repeat (a)–(c), using Δ_0 and deleting the 4's.

10. Over an arbitrary commutative ring, suppose the diagonal quadratic form $Q = ax^2 + \Sigma\, b_i y_i^2$ represents 0 for $x = u$, $y_i = v_i$. Show that Q represents any multiple of $4a^2u^4$. (Set $x = (au^2 + k)u$, $y_i = (au^2 - k)v_i$. Then $Q = 4ka^2u^4$. Compare [21], p. 41.)

11. Show that the conclusion of Theorem 44 is still valid with the hypotheses weakened as follows: the ideal (π) is assumed to be prime, R is allowed to have zero-divisors, and the element π is assumed to be a non-zero-divisor. (Write $Q = ax^2 + bxy + cy^2$, $u = (p, q)$, $w = (r, s)$. Thus $\pi = ap^2 + bpq + cq^2 = ar^2 + brs + cs^2$. Verify that the matrices

$$\begin{pmatrix} apr + bqr + cqs & a(ps - qr) \\ -c(ps - qr) & apr + bps + cqs \end{pmatrix}$$

and

$$\begin{pmatrix} apr - cqs & aps + aqr + bqs \\ cps + cqr + bpr & cqs - apr \end{pmatrix}$$

have determinants p^2 and $-p^2$, respectively. Prove the following: if either matrix has all its entries divisible by p, then after division by p the matrix yields an isometry carrying u into w. Verify that at least one of the matrices must have the desired property, using the equation

$$(apr + bqr + cqs)(apr - cqs) = p(ar^2 - cq^2)$$

as an entering wedge.)

2

ORTHOGONAL SIMILARITY

2-1 The Real Self-Adjoint Case

The main subject in Chapter 2 is the structure of linear transformations on a vector space V, relative to an inner product already given on V.

In this first section we discuss the basic classical case of self-adjoint linear transformations on a Euclidean space, and endeavor to give a simple treatment entirely in real terms.

Definition. Let T be a linear transformation on an inner product space V. We say that T is *self-adjoint* if $(Tx,y) = (x,Ty)$ for all $x, y \in V$.

We delay till later the concept of adjointness, which underlies the use of the word "self-adjoint".

In defining a Euclidean space we wish to operate in as algebraic a manner as possible. So we allow a general real-closed field, instead of confining ourselves to the field of real numbers, and give a definition tailored to our needs.

Definition. A field R is *real-closed* if (1) R is ordered, (2) every positive element in R is a square, (3) every polynomial in one variable over R factors into linear and quadratic factors.

Definition. Let R be a real-closed field. A *Euclidean space* over R is a positive definite finite-dimensional inner product space over R.

If V is a Euclidean space over R, and $x \in V$, then (x,x) is a positive element of R and has a unique positive square root, which we write $|x|$; we call $|x|$ the *norm* (or length) of x.

A basis $\{u_i\}$ of a Euclidean space is *orthonormal* if each $|u_i| = 1$ and

$(u_i,u_j) = 0$ for $i \neq j$. Any Euclidean space has an orthonormal basis (compare Theorem 9, page 11).

We leave to the reader the routine proof of Theorem 45.

Theorem 45. Let T be a linear transformation on a Euclidean space V, and let $\{u_i\}$ be an orthonormal basis of V. Then T is self-adjoint if and only if its matrix relative to $\{u_i\}$ is symmetric.

In the next theorem we record the basic reason that self-adjoint linear transformations have a good chance to admit useful orthogonal decompositions.

Theorem 46. Let T be a self-adjoint linear transformation on an inner product space V. Let W be a subspace invariant under T. Then the orthogonal complement W' is also invariant under T.

Proof. Given $x \in W'$ we must prove $Tx \in W'$. For this we must show $(Tx,W) = 0$, i.e. $(Tx,y) = 0$ for $y \in W$. But $(Tx,y) = (x,Ty)$ since T is self-adjoint, and $(x,Ty) = 0$ since $Ty \in W$ by the invariance of W under T.

Theorem 46 makes it urgent to find invariant subspaces of low dimension. In Theorem 47 we formulate a result that fits our needs.

Theorem 47. Let T be a linear transformation on a vector space V over a field K. Assume that a quadratic polynomial in T is singular, i.e. there exist a, b $\in$ K such that $T^2 + aT + b$ is singular. Then there exists a subspace of V, invariant under T, and of dimension 1 or 2.

Proof. We have $(T^2 + aT + b)x = 0$ for a suitable non-zero x in V. The subspace spanned by x and Tx is invariant under T, and its dimension is 1 or 2.

We are ready for the main theorem of this section.

Theorem 48. Let T be a self-adjoint linear transformation on a finite-dimensional Euclidean space V over a real-closed field R. Then V has an orthonormal basis consisting of vectors characteristic under. T. In particular, the characteristic roots of T are in R.

Proof. There exists a polynomial f such that $f(T) = 0$, e.g. the characteristic polynomial, or the minimal polynomial. Our definition of a real-closed field assures us that f factors into linear and quadratic factors, say $f = g_1g_2 \cdots g_r$. Since $g_1(T)g_2(T) \cdots g_r(T) = 0$, at least one of the terms $g_i(T)$ must be singular. If this g_i is linear we get a characteristic root of T in R, i.e. a one-dimensional invariant subspace. If the g_i in question is quadratic, we get, by Theorem 47, an invariant subspace of dimension 1 or 2.

Let us assume the existence of an invariant subspace W of dimension 2, and make a small computation. Note that W is again a Euclidean space and that T is self-adjoint when restricted to W. Take an orthonormal basis of W, and suppose the matrix of T is

$$\begin{pmatrix} a & b \\ b & c \end{pmatrix}$$

The matrix is symmetric by Theorem 45. The characteristic polynomial of this matrix is $\lambda^2 - (a + c)\lambda + ac - b^2$. For it to have its roots in R,

$$(a + c)^2 - 4(ac - b^2) = (a - c)^2 + 4b^2$$

must be a square in R. This is true, since $(a - c)^2 + 4b^2 \geqq 0$ and positive elements in R are squares.

So we have proved in all cases that T admits a one-dimensional invariant subspace, say S. By Theorem 46, the orthogonal complement S' is also invariant under T. Evidently $V = S \oplus S'$. Any non-zero vector in S can be adjusted to have length 1, and this vector (say u_1) is our choice for the first vector of an orthonormal basis. T is again self-adjoint when restricted to S'. By induction on the dimension, S' has an orthonormal basis u_2, $\cdots$, u_n of vectors characteristic under T. The vectors $u_1, \cdots, u_n$ are the desired orthonormal basis for V.

We assume the reader is familiar with the way an orthogonal matrix implements the passage from one orthonormal basis to another, and we state at once the matrix interpretation of Theorem 48.

Theorem 48a. *Let R be a real-closed field. Then any symmetric matrix A over R is orthogonally similar to a diagonal matrix (i.e. there exists an orthogonal matrix P such that PAP^{-1} is diagonal). Two symmetric matrices over R are orthogonally similar if and only if they have the same characteristic roots (counting multiplicities).*

EXERCISES

1. Prove that the orthogonal matrix P in Theorem 48a can be selected to be proper orthogonal (with determinant 1 rather than -1).

In Exercises 2, 3, and 4, A, B, C are symmetric matrices over a real-closed field. The exhibited matrices are written in block form in terms of smaller matrices.

2. (Cancellation) If

$$\begin{pmatrix} A & 0 \\ 0 & B \end{pmatrix} \quad \text{and} \quad \begin{pmatrix} A & 0 \\ 0 & C \end{pmatrix}$$

are orthogonally similar, prove that B and C are orthogonally similar.

3. (Cutting in half) If

$$\begin{pmatrix} A & 0 \\ 0 & A \end{pmatrix} \quad \text{and} \quad \begin{pmatrix} B & 0 \\ 0 & B \end{pmatrix}$$

are orthogonally similar, prove that A and B are orthogonally similar.

4. (Both together) If

$$\begin{pmatrix} A & & & & \\ & B & & & \\ & & B & & \\ & & & \cdots & \\ & & & & B \end{pmatrix} \quad \text{and} \quad \begin{pmatrix} A & & & & \\ & C & & & \\ & & C & & \\ & & & \cdots & \\ & & & & C \end{pmatrix}$$

are orthogonally similar (there are the same number of copies of B as of C), prove that B and C are orthogonally similar.

5. Let A be a symmetric matrix over a real-closed field. Assume $A^n = I$ for some n. Prove: $A^2 = I$.

6. Let $A_1, \cdots, A_n$ be any matrices over an ordered field. Assume

$$Tr(A_1'A_1 + \cdots + A_n'A_n) = 0$$

where Tr denotes the trace. Prove that each $A_i = 0$.

7. Let V satisfy the axioms for a Euclidean space, except that we waive finite-dimensionality. (Over the real field, V is then called a pre-Hilbert space.) Let $T_1, \cdots, T_n$ be self-adjoint linear transformations on V satisfying $\Sigma\, T_i^2 = 0$. Prove that each $T_i = 0$.

2-2   Unitary Spaces

We now make the transition from the real-closed field R to $K = R(i)$ where $i^2 = -1$. It is a modest exercise in the theory of fields, which we leave to the reader, to see that K is algebraically closed. (Or, if we prefer to get the subject going more quickly, we might add this to the axioms for a real-closed field.) We normally use small Greek letters for elements of K.

The convenience of working with an algebraically closed field is considerable. In many accounts of the subject the "unitary" case is given almost exclusive attention, mainly for this reason. We shall here carry the unitary theory a considerable distance, but then we shall return to the Euclidean case and bring it up to the same point.

The positive definiteness of the inner product is vital and consequently the form we use is Hermitian. Let us take the time to give a complete definition.

   Definition. Let R be a real-closed field and let $K = R(i)$, $i^2 = -1$. Equip K with the involution * of "complex conjugation"; that is, for $\alpha \in K$, $\alpha = a + bi$ with $a, b \in R$, set $\alpha^* = a - bi$. By a *unitary space V* over K we mean a finite-dimensional vector space over K equipped with a positive definite form (,) that is Hermitian relative to *. Thus we have $(y,x) = (x,y)^*$, $(\alpha x,y) = \alpha(x,y)$, $(x,\alpha y) = \alpha^*(x,y)$, and $(x,x) > 0$ for $x \neq 0$. (Note that (x,x) necessarily lies in R.) Like Euclidean spaces, unitary spaces possess orthonormal bases.

We again define self-adjointness of a linear transformation T by $(Tx,y) = (x,Ty)$. Let $A = (a_{ij})$ be the matrix of T relative to an orthonormal basis. Then if T is self-adjoint, $a_{ji} = a_{ij}^*$, and we call the matrix A Hermitian.

Of course any T, self-adjoint or not, possesses a characteristic root and a characteristic vector to go with it (since K is algebraically closed). We can now proceed exactly as in Theorem 48. We state the result.

Theorem 49. For any self-adjoint linear transformation on a unitary space, there exists an orthonormal basis of characteristic vectors.

We move on to expanding the scope of a diagonalization theorem, such as Theorem 49, to a result that is definitive of its kind. We do it in two steps, first taking up commuting sets of self-adjoint linear transformations. A needed preliminary result does not refer to inner products.

Theorem 50. Let $\{T_i\}$ be a commuting set of linear transformations on a finite-dimensional vector space V over an algebraically closed field. Then there exists in V a joint characteristic vector for the T's, i.e. a vector $x \neq 0$ such that each T_ix is a multiple of x.

   Proof. If every T_i is a scalar times the identity, any non-zero vector in V will do. So assume T_1 is not a scalar. Let λ be a characteristic root of T_1, and let W be the set of all x in V with $T_1x = \lambda x$. Then W is a subspace lying strictly between 0 and V. We claim that W is invariant under every T_i. For if x lies in W, then $T_1T_ix = T_iT_1x = \lambda T_ix$, so that $T_ix \in W$.

We look at $\{T_i\}$ as linear transformations on W, and complete the proof by induction on the dimension.

Theorem 51. *Let $\{T_i\}$ be a commuting set of self-adjoint linear trans-formations on a unitary space V. Then V has an orthonormal basis consisting of vectors that are characteristic under every T_i.*

Proof. Apply Theorem 50 to get a joint characteristic vector, and normalize it to u_1, of length 1. By Theorem 46 (equally valid in the unitary case) the orthogonal complement of u_1 is invariant under all the T_i's. Apply induction to complete u_1 to an orthonormal basis of joint characteristic vectors.

From this point on we need the concept of the adjoint of a linear trans-formation. (We chose to get by until now just with self-adjointness in order to reach Theorems 48, 49 and 51 as quickly as possible.)

Theorem 52. *For a linear transformation T on a unitary space V, there exists a unique linear transformation T^* satisfying $(Tx,y) = (x,T^*y)$ for all $x, y \in V$. The mapping $T \rightarrow T^*$ has the following properties: $(T + U)^* = T^* + U^*$, $(TU)^* = U^*T^*$, $T^{**} = T$, $(\alpha T)^* = \alpha^* T^*$ for $\alpha \in K$.*

Proof. In proving the existence of T^* we no longer hesitate (as we did in Chapter 1 up to §1-14) to use the dual space. For any fixed x, the mapping $y \rightarrow (y,x)$ is a linear function on V. In this way we get a linear transformation from V to the dual space of V, and the non-singularity of V tells us that this linear transformation is one-to-one. Hence it is onto as well; i.e., every linear function on V has the form described above.

Now given y and T, we note that $x \rightarrow (Tx,y)$ is a linear function on V. So it is induced by a vector that we define to be T^*y. That $y \rightarrow T^*y$ is linear is a routine verification, and the same is true for all the properties stated in the theorem. We will do one sample: $(TU)^* = U^*T^*$. It is enough to check this on a vector y; and to know $(TU)^*y = U^*T^*y$ it suffices to check the equality after taking inner product with a general vector x. We have, by definition,

$$[x,(TU)^*y] = [(TU)x,y] = (Ux,T^*y) = (x,U^*T^*y)$$

as required.

Suppose that T is represented by the matrix $A = (a_{ij})$ relative to an orthonormal basis. We leave it to the reader to check that T^* is repre-sented by the matrix (a_{ji}^*), for which our notation is A^*.

Call a set S of linear transformations self-adjoint if $T \in S$ implies $T^* \in S$.

Theorem 53. Let S be a self-adjoint set of linear transformations on a unitary space V. Let W be a subspace invariant under S. Then the orthogonal complement W' is also invariant under S.

Proof. The proof is really the same as that of Theorem 46, but we repeat it. For $x \in W'$ and $T \in S$ we need $Tx \in W'$. For this we must show $(Tx,W) = 0$, i.e. $(x,T^*W) = 0$, which is true since $T^* \in S$ implies $T^*W \subset W$.

When can a linear transformation T be diagonalized relative to an orthonormal basis? We note that if we succeed, then T^* will also be diagonal (with conjugate entries down the diagonal). This is our motivation for the next definition.

Definition. A linear transformation T on a unitary space is said to be *normal* if T commutes with T^*.

Normality is sufficient as well as necessary for diagonalization.

Theorem 54. If T is a normal linear transformation on a unitary space V then V has an orthonormal basis consisting of vectors characteristic under T.

Proof. Set $T_1 = T + T^*$, $T_2 = i(T - T^*)$. Then T_1 and T_2 are self-adjoint and commute. We apply Theorem 51, and note $2T = T_1 - iT_2$.

From Theorem 54 we wish to move on to the ultimate in diagonalization: a commutative set of normal linear transformations. For this a bit of additional technique is needed.

Theorem 55. Let $a_1, \cdots, a_n$ be distinct elements of an arbitrary field K. Let $b_1, \cdots, b_n$ be any elements of K. Then there exists a polynomial f in one variable, with coefficients in K, such that $f(a_i) = b_i$ for $i = 1, \cdots, n$.

Proof. We can write down f explicitly. Let $g_i(x)$ be the product of $x - a_1$, $\cdots$, $x - a_n$ with $x - a_i$ deleted, and take

$$f(x) = b_1 \frac{g_1(x)}{g_1(a_1)} + b_2 \frac{g_2(x)}{g_2(a_2)} + \cdots + b_n \frac{g_n(x)}{g_n(a_n)}$$

Theorem 56. Let T be a normal linear transformation on a unitary space. Then T^* can be written as a polynomial in T. T^* commutes with every linear transformation that commutes with T.

Proof. Let $a_1, \cdots, a_k$ be the distinct characteristic roots of T. We apply Theorem 55 to get a polynomial f satisfying $f(a_i) = a_i^*(i = 1, \cdots, k)$. Thinking of T in diagonal form (Theorem 54), we see that $T^* = f(T)$. The final statement of the theorem is an immediate consequence.

Theorem 57. Let $\{T_i\}$ *be a commuting set of normal linear transformations on a unitary space* V. *Then* V *has an orthonormal basis consisting of vectors characteristic under each* T_i.

Proof. By Theorem 56, T_i^* commutes with everything that commutes with T_i, and therefore commutes with T_j. In this way we see that the enlarged set $\{T_i, T_i^*\}$ is commutative. By Theorem 50 there is a joint characteristic vector u_1 for $\{T_i, T_i^*\}$, which we can take to have length 1. By Theorem 53, the orthogonal complement of u_1 is invariant under $\{T_i, T_i^*\}$. We conclude the proof by induction. (Alternative procedure: reduce to a commuting set of self-adjoints as in Theorem 54, and then use Theorem 51.)

EXERCISES

All these exercises deal with linear transformations on a unitary space.

1. We say that T is *skew* if $T^* = -T$, *unitary* if $T^*T = I$ (which is equivalent to $TT^* = I$). Observe that these notions imply normality.
   (a) Prove that a normal linear transformation is skew if and only if its characteristic roots are pure imaginary.
   (b) Prove that a normal linear transformation is unitary if and only if its characteristic roots have absolute value 1.

2. Suppose T normal and U arbitrary. Prove that $TU = 0$ implies $T^*U = 0$.

3. Show that $Tr(\Sigma T_i^* T_i) = 0$ implies $T_i = 0$.

4. Prove that (a) every normal linear transformation is the square of a normal one, (b) every unitary linear transformation is the square of a unitary one. What can one say about the square of a skew linear transformation?

5. Prove: for any linear transformation T there exists an orthonormal basis relative to which T has triangular form. (*Hint:* let x be a characteristic vector of T^*. The orthogonal complement of x is $(n - 1)$-dimensional and invariant under T.)

6. Extend Ex. 5 to a commuting set of linear transformations.

7. Prove that the range of T is the orthogonal complement of the null space of T^*.

8. Prove that if T is normal, T and T^* have the same null space.

9. Prove that if T commutes with T^*T or with $T^*T - TT^*$, then T is normal.

10. Let A, B be normal, T arbitrary. Assume $AT = TB$. Prove $A^*T = TB^*$. (We offer hints for three methods.)

    (1) Use the idea in Theorem 56, working on all the characteristic roots of A and B at once.

    (2) Blow the problem up to 2×2 block matrices

$$\begin{pmatrix} A & 0 \\ 0 & B \end{pmatrix}\begin{pmatrix} 0 & T \\ 0 & 0 \end{pmatrix} = \begin{pmatrix} 0 & T \\ 0 & 0 \end{pmatrix}\begin{pmatrix} A & 0 \\ 0 & B \end{pmatrix}$$

    and use Theorem 56.

    (3) Let $C = AT - TB$. In the four terms of C^*C, two have coefficient 1 and two -1. Check that all four have the same trace, so $Tr(C^*C) = 0$. Use Ex. 3.

11. State the matrix version of Theorem 57.

12. For any T prove that T^*T and TT^* are unitarily equivalent.

13. For a rectangular matrix A, study the relation between the matrices A^*A and AA^*. (Instead of a rectangular matrix, you can talk about a linear transformation between two Euclidean spaces, possibly of different dimensions. The adjoint has a natural definition in this wider context.)

2-3   Positivity and Polar Decomposition

Let V be unitary and T a self-adjoint linear transformation on V. Let us write $f(x,y) = (Tx,y)$. We note that f is another Hermitian inner product, the crucial point being

$$f(y,x) = (Ty,x) = (y,Tx) = (Tx,y)^* = f(x,y)^*$$

Thus from one point of view the study of T amounts to the simultaneous study of two Hermitian forms, one of them positive definite.

    At any rate we may apply to f in turn the point of view of inner product theory. In particular, we distinguish the case where f is positive semi-definite and then call T *positive*. If f is positive definite we shall say that T is *strictly positive*.

    Let us repeat the definitions in direct terms: T is positive if $(Tx,x) \geq 0$ for all x, and T is strictly positive if $(Tx,x) \geq 0$ with equality only for $x = 0$. (It is understood that T has to be self-adjoint before it is eligible for positivity or strict positivity.)

In terms of a diagonalization of T (Theorem 49) we can recast the matter as follows: T is positive if its characteristic roots are positive or 0, strictly positive if its characteristic roots are positive.

It is important to note that for any T, T^*T is positive.

Theorem 58. Let T be any linear transformation on a unitary space. Then T^*T is positive; it is strictly positive if and only if T is non-singular.

Proof. $(T^*Tx,x) = (Tx,Tx) \geqq 0$. If T is singular then $Tx = 0$ for some x, T^*Tx also is 0 and T^*T is not strictly positive. If T is non-singular then $(T^*Tx,x) = (Tx,Tx)$ vanishes only for $x = 0$.

Square roots of positive linear transformations play an important role.

Theorem 59. Let T be a positive linear transformation on a unitary space. Then T has a unique positive square root; it commutes with every linear transformation that commutes with T.

Proof. Take an orthonormal basis of characteristic vectors (Theorem 49) say $u_1, \ldots, u_n$. Suppose $Tu_i = a_i u_i$. Here a_i is a positive element of R (recall that R is the real-closed field from which we got K by adjoining i). Let b_i be the positive square root of a_i, and define H by $Hu_i = b_i u_i$. Then H is positive and $H^2 = T$.

The difficulty in proving H unique is that someone may compute a square root of T in a different basis. To grapple with this, we first prove (as we wish to anyhow) that H commutes with anything that commutes with T. Let f be a polynomial with coefficients in R satisfying $f(b_i) = a_i$ (Theorem 55). Obviously $H = f(T)$ and this makes the double commuting property clear.

Now let H_1 be another positive square root of T. Of course H_1 commutes with T. Hence H and H_1 commute. We can therefore (Theorem 51) diagonalize H and H_1 simultaneously. Now $H^2 = H_1^2$ implies $H = H_1$ at once.

In preparation for Theorem 60, we give a definition at this point (already anticipated in Ex. 1, page 64). A linear transformation U is *unitary* if $(Ux,Uy) = (x,y)$ for all x and y. Equivalent statements are $U^*U = I$ (the identity) and $UU^* = I$.

The reader should keep in mind the polar decomposition $re^{i\theta}$ of a complex number as a motivation for Theorem 60.

Theorem 60. Let T be any linear transformation on a unitary space V. Then T can be written $T = UH$ with H positive and U unitary. In such a *representation H is unique, and is in fact the positive square root of T*T. If T is non-singular, U is also unique.*

We call $T = UH$ a polar decomposition of T. More carefully, we might call it a left (or right?) polar decomposition, there being of course by symmetry a second one $T = H_1U_1$.

Proof. Let us start with the uniqueness of H. From $T = UH$ we get $T^* = HU^*$, $T^*T = HU^*UH = H^2$. So H has to be the positive square root of T^*T, unique by Theorem 59.

Naturally we therefore start constructing the polar decomposition by noting that T^*T is positive (Theorem 58) and taking H to be its positive square root (Theorem 59). When T is non-singular, the discussion finishes swiftly. U has to be TH^{-1}; so much for uniqueness. With the choice $U = TH^{-1}$ we find $U^*U = H^{-1}T^*TH^{-1} = H^{-1}H^2H^{-1} = I$.

When T is singular we have some additional work to do. We are going to have to set $UHx = Tx$ for every x in V. This leads us to define U on the range of H this way. We must pay our respects to the need to check that the proposed definition is unique. In other words, if $Hx = Hy$, we have to prove $Tx = Ty$; or from $Hz = 0$ we must conclude $Tz = 0$. But $(Hz,Hz) = (H^2z,z) = (T^*Tz,z)$, so all is well. Moreover, this shows that U, as defined thus far, is an isometry of the range of H onto the range of T. Now further define U to be an isometry of the orthogonal complement of the range of U onto the orthogonal complement of the range of T. (They have the same dimension, so such an isometry exists, e.g. send an orthonormal basis onto an orthonormal basis.) Then U is unitary on all of V, satisfies $UH = T$, and Theorem 60 is proved.

We add a small supplement to Theorem 60.

*Theorem 61. **If, in Theorem 60, T is normal, then U can be selected to commute with H.***

Proof. We choose to dismiss this by advising the reader to diagonalize T (Theorem 54); the choice of U is then obvious.

Remark. As a matter of fact any choice of U commutes with H (Ex. 2).

EXERCISES

All exercises deal with linear transformations on a unitary space.

1. Suppose the linear transformation T in Theorem 60 is singular. Prove that there are infinitely many choices for U in the polar decomposition $T = UH$.

2. Prove (as asserted above) that in Theorem 61 any choice of U commutes with H.

3. Let T be any normal linear transformation, n any positive integer. Show that T has a normal n-th root that commutes with everything that commutes with T.

4. Let T be self-adjoint and n odd. Prove that T has exactly one self-adjoint n-th root.

5. Let T be positive and n even. Prove that T has exactly one positive n-th root.

6. Let A be strictly positive, B self-adjoint. Prove that $A + iB$ is non-singular.

7. Let A, B be strictly positive. Prove $\det(A + B) > \det(A)$.

8. For A, B self-adjoint we define $A \geq B$ to mean that $A - B$ is positive. (a) If $A \geq B$, is $A^2 \geq B^2$? (b) Let A, B be positive, C and D their positive square roots. Does $A \geq B$ imply $C \geq D$?

9. If A and B are normal and similar, prove that they are unitarily similar. (This can be done by diagonalization and comparison of characteristic roots. For a conceptual approach that leads to useful generalizations, see the next exercise.)

10. Let A and B be arbitrary (not necessarily normal) linear transformations on a unitary space. Prove that A and B are unitarily equivalent if and only if the pair A, A^* is simultaneously similar to the pair B, B^*, i.e., there exists a non-singular P with $P^{-1}AP = B$, $P^{-1}A^*P = B^*$. (*Hint:* necessity is obvious; take * in $U^*AU = B$. For sufficiency, * the second equation and combine with the first to get $PP^*A = APP^*$. In $P = HU$, H commutes with A, so $U^*AU = B$.)

11. Suppose A and AB are normal. Prove the following statements equivalent:
(a) B commutes with A^*A,
(b) BA is normal.
For (a) → (b), use $A = UH$ and get $U^*ABU = BA$. For (b) → (a), apply Ex. 10, page 65 to $(AB)A = A(BA)$, to get $B^*A^*A = AA^*B$.

12. If A, B, and AB are normal prove that BA is normal. (By Ex. 11 it suffices to prove that B commutes with A^*A. Let $C = BA^*A - A^*AB$, and check $Tr(C^*C) = 0$. Exs. 11 and 12 come from [25], which in turn was inspired by [41].)

13. If A is positive and B self-adjoint, prove that the characteristic roots of AB are real. (Write $A = H^2$. Pass from $AB = H^2B$ to HBH, using the fact that for any matrices P and Q, PQ and QP have the same characteristic roots.)

14. If A and B are positive, prove that AB has characteristic roots ≥ 0.

15. If A and B are strictly positive, prove that AB is similar to a positive definite linear transformation (use the device in Ex. 13).

16. Suppose that A, B, C are strictly positive, and ABC self-adjoint. Prove that ABC is strictly positive. (Write $A = H^2$, H strictly positive. $AB = HDH^{-1}$, $BA = H^{-1}DH$ where $D = HBH$ is strictly positive. Let f be polynomial

giving square root on the characteristic roots of D, $f(D) = E$, $E^2 = D$, $f(AB) = HEH^{-1}$, $f(BA) = H^{-1}EH$. Our hypothesis says $ABC = CBA$. Hence $f(AB)C = Cf(BA)$, $HEH^{-1}C = CH^{-1}EH$, $ABC = (HEH^{-1})^2C = HEH^{-1}CH^{-1}EH$, which is strictly positive. This exercise comes from [42]; the proof sketched is copied from a postcard from Halmos dated July 10, 1963.)

17. For any linear transformations A and B, prove that there exist unitary linear transformations U_1 and U_2 with $U_1AU_2 = B$ if and only if A^*A is unitarily equivalent to B^*B. Extend to the "rectangular" case (see Ex. 13, page 65.)

2-4   The Real Case, Continued

The definition and properties of the adjoint (Theorem 52) are essentially the same in Euclidean spaces as in unitary space (in fact, a little easier since there is no disturbance caused by complex conjugation). Moreover, Theorems 51, 53, 58, 59 and 60 go through virtually unchanged. It is the material on normal linear transformations that needs reconsideration.

We define normality in the same way: by the property that T commutes with T^*. One fact we want is the portion of Theorem 56 asserting that T^* commutes with everything that commutes with T. Of the various ways this might be done, we shall officially suggest the method sketched in the third hint for Ex. 10, page 65. At any rate, we shall state it as a formal theorem.

Theorem 61. *Let T be a normal linear transformation on a Euclidean space. Then T^* commutes with every linear transformation that commutes with T.*

Beyond this, our objective is the analysis of a commutative set of normal linear transformations (Theorem 62). We approach it in several stages.

(1) *A single skew linear transformation*   We call T skew if $T^* = -T$. We analyze T by first quoting Theorem 47 to get an invariant subspace W of dimension 1 or 2. If W is one-dimensional, $TW = 0$. If W is two-dimensional, then relative to any orthonormal basis of W the matrix of T is skew-symmetric and has the form

$$(22) \qquad \begin{pmatrix} 0 & a \\ -a & 0 \end{pmatrix}$$

This is virtually a canonical form, and becomes one if we select a to be positive (as we can do by interchanging the basis vectors if necessary).

By Theorem 46, the orthogonal complement W' is again invariant under T. (Strictly speaking we should harmlessly enlarge T to the set $\{T, -T\}$ before quoting Theorem 46.) So: the upshot is that relative to a suitable orthonormal basis of V, T has the form

$$
\begin{pmatrix}
0 & a & & & & & & & & \\
-a & 0 & & & & & & & & \\
& & 0 & b & & & & & & \\
& & -b & 0 & & & & & & \\
& & & & \cdot & & & & & \\
& & & & & \cdot & & & & \\
& & & & & & 0 & c & & \\
& & & & & & -c & 0 & & \\
& & & & & & & & 0 & \cdot \quad \cdot \quad \cdot \quad 0 \\
& & & & & & & & & \cdot \qquad\qquad \cdot \\
& & & & & & & & & \cdot \qquad\qquad \cdot \\
& & & & & & & & & \cdot \qquad\qquad \cdot \\
& & & & & & & & 0 & \cdot \quad \cdot \quad \cdot \quad 0
\end{pmatrix}
$$

(2) *A self-adjoint set containing a commuting skew* We are given $\{T_i, T_i{}^*\}$, including among them a skew T which commutes with them all. Theorem 46 tells us that if W is invariant under $\{T_i, T_i{}^*\}$ so is W', and we get a decomposition $V = W \oplus W'$. Thus the crucial thing to analyze is the case where V is irreducible, i.e. where the only invariant subspaces are 0 and V.

Suppose (22) is one of the blocks occurring in T. Then the null space W of $T^2 + aI$ is not 0. Furthermore W is invariant under each T_i; if $x \in W$ then $0 = T_i(T^2 + aI)x = (T^2 + aI)T_ix$, so that $T_ix \in W$. Assuming irreducibility we thus get that W is all of V, i.e. $T^2 = -aI$. (What we have just done is in essence a special case of something called Schur's lemma).

(3) *A commuting set of self-adjoints and skews* We again assume V irreducible. Assume $T \neq 0$ is a skew linear transformation in the set. By what we have just shown, $T^2 = -aI$. Here $a \neq 0$, and in particular, T is non-singular. Now if T_i is skew and commutes with T, then T_iT is self-adjoint. Our problem is unchanged if we replace T_i by T_iT. So we now have a commuting set consisting of T and a number of self-adjoint linear transformations. The argument in Theorem 50 (which is exactly like the argument in (2) above) shows that each of these self-adjoint linear transformations is a scalar. The upshot: V is two-dimensional.

(4) *A commuting set of normal linear transformations* By Theorem 61 we can throw in all adjoints and still have a commuting set. Then replace T

and T^* by $T + T^*$ and $T - T^*$, which are respectively self-adjoint and skew. Part (3) applies, to decompose V into an orthogonal direct sum of one- and two-dimensional pieces. Note that on each irreducible two-dimensional piece the self-adjoint linear transformations are scalars. We have proved:

Theorem 62. *Let* $\{T_i\}$ *be a commuting set of normal linear transformations on a Euclidean space* V. *Then* V *is an orthogonal direct sum of invariant subspaces, each of dimension 1 or 2, and on the two-dimensional summands each* T_i *has the form*

$$\begin{pmatrix} a_i & b_i \\ -b_i & a_i \end{pmatrix}$$

EXERCISES

The linear transformations are on a Euclidean space.

1. We say T is *orthogonal* if $(Tx, Ty) = (x, y)$ for all x and y. Prove that for an orthogonal T there exists an orthonormal basis with 1×1 blocks having an entry ± 1, and 2×2 blocks

$$\begin{pmatrix} a & b \\ -b & a \end{pmatrix}$$

with $a^2 + b^2 = 1$, $b \neq 0$. (This is as close as we shall come to trigonometric functions in this book!)

2. Let T be normal. Prove that T is orthogonal if and only if its characteristic roots have absolute value 1, and that T is skew if and only if its characteristic roots are pure imaginary.

2-5   Specht's Theorem

We devote this section to a general theorem on unitary equivalence due to Specht [33]. It seems natural to state it in terms of matrices.

Theorem 63. *Let* R *be a real-closed field,* $K = R(i)$. *Let* A *and* B *be* $n \times n$ *matrices over* K. *Then* A *and* B *are unitarily equivalent if for every "word"* $A^i A^{*i} A^k A^{*l} \cdots$ *in* A *and* A^* *we have*

$$Tr(A^i A^{*i} A^k A^{*l} \cdots) = Tr(B^i B^{*i} B^k B^{*l} \cdots)$$

Remarks. 1. The condition is trivially necessary. If $U*AU = B$, U unitary, then (take *) we also have $U*A*U = B*$, and so conjugation by U carries any word in A and $A*$ into the corresponding word in B and $B*$.

2. The theorem is not offered as a practical test for unitary equivalence— the infinite number of tests required speaks for itself. Pearcy's reduction [31] to 4^{n^2} words is not a big help either. But as a crisp criterion, easily worked with for theoretical purposes, it leaves little to be desired. As evidence we offer two favorite exercises (1 and 2): cancellation, and sub-division into equal parts.

3. Let us note that the normal case is subsumed in a satisfactory way. If A is normal, then the characteristic roots of A are all that is needed, and they are determined by the traces of the first n powers of A.

4. The general spirit of Specht's theorem nevertheless lies in a different direction: it is, in disguise, really a theorem about algebras and their representations. It would take quite a bit of space to give the proof in full. More to the point, it would be out of proportion; the necessary ring theory should be developed as a coherent doctrine of its own.

We shall consequently confine ourselves to a sketch, which should suffice for a reader who knows the elements of ring theory.

Sketch of proof of Theorem 63. Let α be the algebra generated by A and $A*$, $\mathfrak{B}$ that generated by B and $B*$. We propose to define an algebra iso-morphism ϕ of α onto $\mathfrak{B}$, satisfying $\phi(A) = B$, $\phi(A*) = B*$. The crucial point is this: suppose C is a (non-commutative) polynomial in A and $A*$, i.e. a linear combination, with coefficients in K, of words of the sort occur-ring in the theorem. Let D be the same linear combination of the corre-sponding words in B, $B*$. To have ϕ well-defined, we need to know that $C = 0$ implies $D = 0$. Now $C = 0$ implies $Tr(C*C) = 0$. The hypothesis of the theorem applies, to yield $Tr(C*C) = Tr(D*D)$; first we have equality of traces for the words occurring in $C*C$ and $D*D$, and then we use linearity of the trace. Hence $Tr(D*D) = 0$, whence $D = 0$.

Now we can change our point of view and think of a single algebra α and two representations of it. Because of the self-adjointness and positive definiteness present, α is semi-simple. Any representation is a direct sum of irreducible ones, and the isomorphism classes of irreducible representa-tions of α are in one-to-one correspondence with the simple components of α. Given a simple component, we have only to determine the multiplicity of the corresponding irreducible representation. But this is determined by $Tr(E)$ where E is the central idempotent for the simple component.

If we return to the two algebras α and $\mathfrak{B}$, the upshot of this is that the isomorphism ϕ is induced by a linear transformation P of V onto itself. In other words $P^{-1}AP = B$. This P need not be unitary. This can be remedied by reviewing the whole argument, keeping track of the *-structure throughout, so that the P that arises will be unitary. Or we can, as a final finishing touch, switch from P to a unitary linear transformation by a polar decomposition argument (compare Ex. 10, page 68).

EXERCISES

1. If the matrices

$$\begin{pmatrix} A & 0 \\ 0 & B \end{pmatrix} \quad \text{and} \quad \begin{pmatrix} A & 0 \\ 0 & C \end{pmatrix}$$

are unitarily equivalent, prove that B and C are unitarily equivalent.
2. If the direct sum of n copies of the matrix A is unitarily equivalent to a similar direct sum for B, prove A and B unitarily equivalent.

2-6   Remarks on Similarity

Excellent treatments of similarity abound in textbooks suitable for a first course in linear algebra. We have therefore decided to assume familiarity on the part of the reader with the basic aspects of the theory of similarity. In this section, after a brief review of the high spots, we add several remarks.

(1) *The matrix method*   Let A be a square matrix over the field K. We associate with A the matrix $xI - A$ over the polynomial ring $K[x]$. Classification of A under similarity turns out to coincide with classification of $xI - A$ under equivalence (left and right multiplication by unimodular matrices, i.e. matrices over $K[x]$ with determinant a non-zero constant). Since $K[x]$ is a principal ideal ring, the equivalence invariants of $A - xI$ are its invariant factors.

(2) *The module method*   Let V be a vector space (it can be infinite-dimensional) over a field K. Let T be a linear transformation on V. With $R = K[x]$, x an indeterminate, we convert V into an R-module by having x act on V the way T does. Classification of T under similarity is the same as classification, under isomorphism, of V as an R-module. If V is finite-dimensional, the theory of finitely generated modules over a principal ideal ring is available, and leads to the same invariant factors obtained by the matrix method.

(3) *Rational canonical form*   The vector space is a direct sum of invariant subspaces, one for each invariant factor. Corresponding to an invariant factor

$$f(x) = x^n - a_1 x^{n-1} - \cdots - a_{n-1} - a_n$$

there is a basis making the matrix take the form of the companion matrix of f:

$$(23) \quad \begin{pmatrix} 0 & 1 & 0 & 0 & \cdot & \cdot & 0 & 0 \\ 0 & 0 & 1 & 0 & \cdot & \cdot & 0 & 0 \\ & & & \cdot & & & \cdot & \\ 0 & 0 & 0 & \cdot & \cdot & \cdot & 0 & 1 \\ a_n & a_{n-1} & \cdot & \cdot & \cdot & \cdot & a_2 & a_1 \end{pmatrix}$$

(4) *Jordan canonical form*   When the base field K is algebraically closed, it is natural to decompose the invariant factors into powers of linear factors (*elementary divisors*). Then there is a second canonical form (Jordan) which is generally simpler to use; it attaches to the polynomial $(x-a)^n$ the matrix

$$(24) \quad \begin{pmatrix} a & 1 & 0 & \cdot & \cdot & 0 & 0 \\ 0 & a & 1 & 0 & \cdot & 0 & 0 \\ & & & \cdot & \cdot & \cdot & \\ 0 & 0 & \cdot & \cdot & \cdot & a & 1 \\ 0 & 0 & \cdot & \cdot & \cdot & 0 & a \end{pmatrix}$$

We offer a remark on the connection between the matrix method and the module method, which seems first to have been made in the Ph.D. thesis of A. Buccino (Chicago, 1967). Let V have basis $u_1, \cdots, u_n$ and let the linear transformation T satisfy $Tu_i = \Sigma\, a_{ij} u_j$, so that the matrix of T is $A = (a_{ij})$. We make V into an R-module, $R = K[x]$, as described above. Then $u_1, \cdots, u_n$ serve to generate V (a fortiori) as an R-module. The relations

$$(25) \quad \begin{aligned} (x - a_{11})u_1 - a_{12}u_2 - \cdots - a_{1n}u_n &= 0 \\ -a_{21}u_1 + (x - a_{22})u_2 - \cdots - a_{2n}u_n &= 0 \\ \cdot \qquad \cdot \qquad \cdot \qquad \cdot \quad& \\ -a_{n1}u_1 - a_{n2}u_2 - \cdots + (x - a_{nn})u_n &= 0 \end{aligned}$$

are satisfied. Now a very simple argument shows that the relations (25) generate all relations on $u_1, \cdots, u_n$. So we have a natural interpretation of

$xI - A$; it is a matrix of relations for the generators $u_1, \cdots, u_n$ of the R–module V. Now it is standard that changing the matrix of relations by equivalence leaves the isomorphism class of the module unchanged.

In all this K could actually have been any commutative ring with unit. Thus we have a conceptual proof of the following theorem:

Theorem 64. *Let A and B be square matrices over K, a commutative ring with unit. Then A and B are similar over K if and only if $xA - I$ and $xB - I$ are equivalent over the polynomial ring $K[x]$.*

There are two notable consequences of the theory of similarity: (1) similarity over a field containing K implies similarity over K, (2) any matrix is similar to its transpose. We make a comment on each.

(1) This of course is seen from the fact that the computation of the invariant factors of $xI - A$ would be exactly the same, even if a larger field were available. But the reader should know that there exists also a successful frontal attack on the problem, which has the advantage of working just as well for sets of matrices. We quote [20], p. 223, for a proof and shall not reproduce it here. (Actually Jacobson handles the case of an infinite field, and refers to Deuring [10] for the finite case.) The device of polar decomposition enables us to transfer this theorem to the unitary-orthogonal setup.

Theorem 65. *Let R be a real-closed field, $K = R(i)$. Let $\{A_j\}$, $\{B_j\}$ be sets of matrices over R, and suppose they are simultaneously unitarily equivalent over K, that is, there exists a unitary matrix U such that $U^*A_jU = B_j$ for all j. Then $\{A_j\}$ and $\{B_j\}$ are simultaneously orthogonally equivalent over R.*

Proof. Taking $*$ in $U^*A_jU = B_j$ gives us $U^*A_j^*U = B_j^*$. Thus U actually implements a simultaneous unitary equivalence of the enlarged sets $\{A_j, A_j^*\}$ and $\{B_j, B_j^*\}$. Now we can quote the above theorem at least to get simultaneous *similarity* over R, that is, there exists a nonsingular matrix P with entries in R satisfying $P^{-1}A_jP = B_j$, $P^{-1}A_j^*P = B_j^*$. For the passage from P to an orthogonal matrix we quote Ex. 10, page 68. (It is valid virtually without change in the real case.)

We note that Theorem 65 makes it clear that Specht's theorem (Theorem 63) is equally valid in the real case; this was noted by Pearcy [31]. Alternatively, we can convince ourselves that the proof sketched in §2-5 extends to the real case.

(2) A and its transpose A' are similar because $xI - A'$ is a transpose of $xI - A$, and over a principal ideal ring any matrix is equivalent to its transpose.

Suppose P implements the similarity of A and A'. We can rewrite $P^{-1}AP = A'$ as $AP = PA'$. Taking transposes we get $P'A' = AP'$. We can add the two equations to get $AQ = QA'$, where Q is the symmetric matrix $P + P'$. If Q were non-singular, we would have achieved what we shall call *symmetric similarity* of A and A', and a consequence would be $A = QA'Q^{-1}$, an expression of A as a product of two symmetric matrices, since $(QA')' = AQ = QA'$. The next theorem (due to Voss [38]) shows that such a Q can be found. The proof, incidentally, contains a nice application of the rational canonical form.

Theorem 66. *Let A be a square matrix over an arbitrary field. Then A is symmetrically similar to its transpose A', and A can be expressed as a product of two symmetric matrices.*

Proof. We handle the proof in "concrete" matrix style, first observing that the problem is invariant under similarity. We assume $D^{-1}AD$ to be symmetrically similar to its transpose $D'A'D'^{-1}$:

(26) $$D'A'D'^{-1} = P^{-1}D^{-1}ADP$$

with P symmetric. We deduce from (26) that $A' = E^{-1}AE$, where E is the symmetric matrix DPD'.

Suppose the matrix A splits in block diagonal form:

$$\begin{pmatrix} A_1 & & & & \\ & A_2 & & & \\ & & \cdot & & \\ & & & \cdot & \\ & & & & \cdot \\ & & & & & A_k \end{pmatrix}$$

It suffices to prove our theorem for a single block. So we can assume A to be the companion matrix (23). Before doing this we note that if we could assume A to be a Jordan block (24), then a symmetric P with $P^{-1}AP$ is easily written down, namely the "anti-diagonal" matrix

$$\begin{pmatrix} 0 & 0 & 0 & \cdot & \cdot & \cdot & 0 & 1 \\ 0 & 0 & 0 & \cdot & \cdot & \cdot & 1 & 0 \\ & & & \cdot & \cdot & \cdot & & \\ 0 & 1 & 0 & \cdot & \cdot & \cdot & 0 & 0 \\ 1 & 0 & 0 & \cdot & \cdot & \cdot & 0 & 0 \end{pmatrix}$$

For the companion matrix (23) the matter is more complicated, but a suitable P can still be written down reasonably explicitly:

$$P = \begin{pmatrix} 0 & 0 & 0 & \cdot & \cdot & \cdot & 0 & 1 \\ 0 & 0 & 0 & \cdot & \cdot & \cdot & 1 & s_1 \\ 0 & 0 & 0 & \cdot & \cdot & 1 & s_1 & s_2 \\ & & & & & \cdot & \cdot & s_3 \\ & & & & & & \cdot & \\ & & & \cdot & \cdot & \cdot & & \\ & & & \cdot & & \cdot & & \\ 0 & 0 & 1 & s_1 & \cdot & \cdot & & \\ 0 & 1 & s_1 & s_2 & \cdot & & & s_{n-2} \\ 1 & s_1 & s_2 & s_3 & & & s_{n-2} & s_{n-1} \end{pmatrix}$$

where the elements $s_1, s_2, \cdots, s_{n-1}$ are determined recursively by the equations

$$s_1 = a_1$$
$$s_2 = s_1 a_1 + a_2$$
$$s_3 = s_2 a_1 + s_1 a_2 + a_3$$
$$s_4 = s_3 a_1 + s_2 a_2 + s_1 a_3 + a_4$$

$$\cdot \qquad \cdot \qquad \cdot$$

Remark. We have in effect given an explicit recursive formula for P, but we could have shortened the discussion by showing that any P has to be symmetric [35].

2-7 Orthogonal Similarity over Algebraically Closed Fields

If we study orthogonal similarity over fields that are not real closed there is in general no diagonalization theorem such as Theorem 48. But this does not mean that hope for a useful theory must be abandoned. We can also regard Theorem 48 as saying (in part) that if two symmetric matrices are similar, then they are orthogonally similar. Stated this way, we have a problem that makes sense. We proceed to prove that (over algebraically closed fields of characteristic $\neq 2$) there is a correct theorem to this effect.

The technique rests, in effect, on still another application of polar decomposition. A scrutiny of our discussion of polar decomposition shows that, at least for non-singular linear transformations, the crucial point was the existence of a suitable square root.

We prove what is needed in two steps, first discussing linear transformations which have all their characteristic roots equal to 1. Otherwise described, such a linear transformation has the form identity plus nilpotent, and the convenient name *unipotent* has become standard.

Theorem 67. *Let T be a unipotent linear transformation on a vector space over a field K of characteristic $\neq 2$. Then there exists a polynomial in T whose square is T.*

Proof. Write $T = I + N$, N nilpotent. One method of proof is to use the binomial expansion of $(I + N)^{1/2}$. Since N is nilpotent, the series actually terminates in a finite number of steps, and yields a polynomial in N (i.e. a polynomial in T). It turns out that the binomial coefficients that occur are all rational numbers with odd denominators. Checking this, and convincing ourselves that we are really getting a square root of T, would require a little attention. So we offer an alternative stepwise construction. We assert that it is possible to find elements $b_1, \cdots, b_k \in K$ such that

$$(I + b_1 N + b_2 N^2 + \cdots + b_k N^k)^2 - (I + N)$$

has powers only from N^{k+1} up. (In fact, the b's will be in the prime subfield of K.) For $k = 1$, $b_1 = \frac{1}{2}$ will do. Supposing the statement true for k, we shall prove it for $k + 1$. Write $Z = b_1 N + \cdots + b_k N^k$, and suppose $(I + Z)^2 - (I + N) = cN^{k+1} +$ higher terms. Then

$$(I + Z + b_{k+1} N^{k+1})^2 - (I + N)$$
$$= (2b_{k+1} + c)N^{k+1} + \text{higher terms}$$

so we have only to set $b_{k+1} = -c/2$. Since some power of N is 0, this procedure will in due course yield a polynomial in N that is a square root of $I + N = T$.

Theorem 68. *Let T be a non-singular linear transformation on a finite-dimensional vector space over an algebraically closed field K of characteristic $\neq 2$. Then there is a polynomial in T whose square is T.*

Proof. Let $\lambda_1, \cdots, \lambda_r$ be the distinct characteristic roots of T. Let $V(\lambda_i)$ be the characteristic subspace corresponding to λ_i, i.e. $V(\lambda_i)$ is the set of all vectors annihilated by some power of $T - \lambda_i I$. One knows that each $V(\lambda_i)$ is invariant under T and that V is the vector space direct sum

$$V = V(\lambda_1) \oplus \cdots \oplus V(\lambda_r)$$

Write T_i for the restriction of T to $V(\lambda_i)$. We have that $\lambda_i^{-1}T_i$ is uni-potent. Write X_i for the linear transformation provided by Theorem 67, i.e., X_i is a polynomial in $\lambda_i^{-1}T_i$ and $X_i^2 = \lambda_i^{-1}T_i$. Set $Y_i = \sqrt{\lambda_i X_i}$; then $Y_i^2 = T_i$ and Y_i is a polynomial in T_i, say $Y_i = f_i(T_i)$.

Suppose that $(T_i - \lambda_i I)^{n_i} = 0$. Since the polynomials $(x - \lambda_i)^{n_i}$ are relatively prime, it is possible to solve the congruences

$$(27) \qquad g \equiv f_i \bmod (x - \lambda_i)^{n_i} \quad (i = 1, \cdots, r)$$

for a polynomial g. Set $Y = g(T)$. We claim that $Y^2 = T$. It is enough to check this on each $V(\lambda_i)$ where it follows from (27).

We are ready for one more application of the polar decomposition trick.

Theorem 69. Let V be a non-singular finite-dimensional inner product space over an algebraically closed field of characteristic $\neq 2$. Let A and B be linear transformations on V such that the pair A, B, is simultaneously similar to the pair A^*, B^*, i.e. there exists a non-singular linear transformation P satisfying $P^{-1}AP = B$, $P^{-1}A^*P = B^*$. Then A and B are orthogonally similar.

Proof. Our equations read $AP = PB$ and $A^*P = PB^*$. Take $*$ in the second, to get $P^*A = BP^*$. This combines with the first equation to yield $PP^*A = APP^*$, i.e. PP^* commutes with A. Now let H be the linear transformation provided by Theorem 68, so that H is a polynomial in PP^* and $H^2 = PP^*$. We have that $H^* = H$ and H commutes with A. Set $U = H^{-1}P$. Then $UU^* = H^{-1}PP^*H^{-1} = I$, U is orthogonal, and $U^*AU = U^{-1}AU = P^{-1}HAH^{-1}P = P^{-1}AP = B$.

The interesting application of Theorem 69 is to cases where the behaviour of A determines that of A^*.

Theorem 70. Let V be a non-singular finite-dimensional inner product space over an algebraically closed field of characteristic $\neq 2$. Let A and B be linear transformations on V that are both self-adjoint, or both skew, or both orthogonal. Then similarity of A and B implies orthogonal similarity.

Proof. In each case $P^{-1}AP = B$ implies $P^{-1}A^*P = B^*$, so Theorem 69 is applicable.

Shall we abandon characteristic 2 without a fight? As discouraging evidence we note what happens in the very first case. Over a field K of characteristic 2 all the matrices

(28)
$$\begin{pmatrix} a & a \\ a & a \end{pmatrix} \qquad a \neq 0$$

are symmetric and similar (they are nilpotent of index 2). But no two are orthogonally similar, for a direct small computation shows that the general 2×2 orthogonal matrix has the form

(29)
$$\begin{pmatrix} 1+p & p \\ p & 1+p \end{pmatrix}$$

p ranging over K. We verify that conjugation by the matrix (29) leaves the matrix (28) fixed.

There is more to be said here, including an examination of quadratic forms rather than symmetric bilinear forms. But we shall conclude on an affirmative note by proving a theorem analogous to Theorem 70 in the characteristic 2 alternate case.

Let V be a finite-dimensional vector space over a field K of characteristic 2. Assume that V carries a non-singular alternate form (,). The linear transformations we are going to study are to have the property $(Ax,x) = 0$ for all x in V. We call such an A *alternate;* note that by linearizing we get that A is self-adjoint. A mapping of V one-to-one onto itself preserving the inner product is called *symplectic.* In these terms the theorem reads as follows:

Theorem 71. *Let V be a finite-dimensional vector space over an algebraically closed field of characteristic 2. Assume that V carries a non-singular alternate form. Let A and B be alternate linear transformations on V. Then similarity of A and B implies symplectic similarity of A and B.*

Proof. No polar decomposition device appears to exist, so our only recourse is to launch a frontal assault. We shall examine the structure of an alternate A and in effect give a canonical form. The argument (with tiny changes) is equally valid for self-adjoint linear transformations on inner product spaces of characteristic $\neq 2$, and furnishes a different proof for the self-adjoint case of Theorem 70.

We first show that the characteristic subspaces of A are orthogonal. Let λ and μ be distinct characteristic roots of A. Let $x \in A(\lambda)$, $y \in A(\mu)$. Thus we have $(A - \lambda I)^r x = (A - \mu I)^s y = 0$ for suitable integers r and s. Now the polynomials $(z - \lambda)^r$ and $(z - \mu)^s$ are relatively prime, z being an indeterminate. Therefore we can find polynomials $g(z)$ and $h(z)$ such that

$$(30) \qquad g(z)(z - \lambda)^r + h(z)(z - \mu)^s = 1$$

In (30) replace z by A and apply both sides to the vector y. The result is $y = (A - \lambda I)^r w$ where $w = g(A)y$. Then

$$(x,y) = (x, (A - \lambda I)^r w) = ((A - \lambda I)^r x, w) = 0$$

Thus the problem of studying the structure of A has been reduced to the case where A has one characteristic root. By subtracting that characteristic root, we arrange that A is nilpotent. Say $A^k = 0$ with k minimal.

We are going to show that V has a $2k$-dimensional invariant subspace that is an orthogonal direct summand of V and has a structure fully describable in advance. Iteration of this procedure determines A completely, and proves Theorem 71.

Pick x with $A^{k-1}x \neq 0$ and then y with $(A^{k-1}x,y) \neq 0$. We can assume $(A^{k-1}x,y) = 1$. We proceed to make a better choice of y. Write $(y,A^{k-i}x) = c_i$ for $i = 2, \cdots, k$. Solve the equations

$$d_2 + c_2 = 0$$
$$d_3 + d_2c_2 + c_3 = 0$$
$$d_4 + d_3c_2 + d_2c_3 + c_4 = 0$$
$$\cdot \quad \cdot \quad \cdot$$
$$d_k + d_{k-1}c_2 + \cdots + d_2c_{k-1} + c_k = 0$$

in succession for $d_2, \cdots, d_k$ and set $u = y + d_2Ay + d_3A^2y + \cdots + d_kA^{k-1}y$. Then $(u,A^{k-1}x) = 1$ has been maintained. What has been achieved can be exhibited by the tableau

$$x, \quad Ax, \quad \cdots, A^{k-2}x, A^{k-1}x$$
$$A^{k-1}u, A^{k-2}u, \cdots, \quad Au, \quad u$$

The inner product of any vector in the first row with the vector underneath it is 1, and all other inner products are 0. These facts show that the $2k$ vectors in question are linearly independent, and indeed they form a symplectic basis for the subspace W they span. Of course W is an orthogonal direct summand of V. Since the action of A on W is unique, the proof is finished.

Theorems 70 and 71 are only an introduction to a large topic. For an extensive discussion and earlier references, see Wall [40].

EXERCISES

Remark. Theorems 70 and 71 were in effect *uniqueness* theorems for certain linear transformations. Untouched, but perhaps equally important, is the question of *existence*.

1. Let A and V be as in Theorem 71. Prove that the elementary divisors of A come in pairs. Prove that there exists an alternate A with prescribed elementary divisors, provided the latter come in pairs. (A little scrutiny of the proof of Theorem 71 is all that is needed.)

2. Let V be as in Theorem 70. Show that any linear transformation on V is similar to a self-adjoint one. (Reduce to the nilpotent case, say $T^n = 0$. It suffices to exhibit an example with a single elementary divisor. Simplest choice: $(T^i x, T^j x) = 1$ for $i + j = n - 1$, otherwise 0.)

3. With V as in Theorem 70, and T a linear transformation on V, give necessary and sufficient conditions for T to be similar to a skew linear transformation. (Answer: for $\lambda \neq 0$, the elementary divisors for λ and $-\lambda$ must match. For $\lambda = 0$, the elementary divisors must have even degrees and must occur in pairs.)

4. Let V be as in Theorem 71. (a) Let A and B be symplectic linear transformations on V. Prove that if A and B are similar, they are symplectically similar. (b) Give necessary and sufficient conditions on the elementary divisors of a linear transformation T for it to be similar to a symplectic one.

3

GEOMETRY

3-1 Affine Planes

We start our study of geometry with the simplest object: an affine plane. We shall in due course recognize how badly it needs to be completed to a projective plane. But an affine plane can be treated in such an elementary way, and meshes so well with linear algebra, that it is the appropriate starting point.

For quite some time we shall stick to the two-dimensional case over a (commutative) field. The additional things that need to be said for higher dimension, or for a non-commutative underlying division ring, are deferred to Sections 3-9 and 3-10.

Fix a field K, and a two-dimensional vector space V over K. That is all there is to an affine plane. However, when we think of V geometrically, we write Π for it.

The *points* of Π are the vectors of V. The *lines* of Π are not only the one-dimensional subspaces (lines through the origin) but their cosets. From one point of view the crux of the matter is this: we are stripping the origin of its privileged position, and putting all points and lines on the same footing.

Let us fix our notation. In an affine plane the letters x and y are so traditional for the coordinates of a point that we shall stay away from them (except when we do introduce coordinates). We shall instead adhere to geometric tradition and use capital Latin letters for points—except that L, M, N are reserved for lines, V for the vector space, W for a one-dimensional subspace, and T, U for linear transformations. We observe that points such as A and B are elements of V and therefore support the vector space operations $A + B$, cA, $\cdots$.

A typical line L has the form $A + W$. Here W is unique, but A can be changed by a member of W. Observe that W is the parallel line through the origin (Fig. 1).

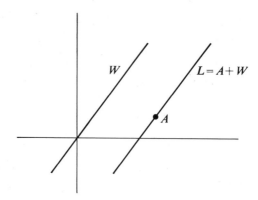

Figure 1

We now proceed with a numbered list of remarks, all too modest to be dignified as theorems.

(1) *Through two distinct points A and B there is exactly one line.* If W is the one-dimensional subspace spanned by $B - A$, the line we want is $L = A + W$. Clearly it passes through A and B. Any line through A has the form $A + W_1$, and if this is to contain B, W_1 has to contain $B - A$. Thus $W = W_1$.

As in elementary geometry, we write AB for the line joining A and B.

(2) *Two distinct lines meet in at most one point.* This is immediate from (1).

We call two lines *parallel* if they do not meet.

(3) *Given a line L and a point C not on L, there is exactly one line through C parallel to L.* Say $L = A + W$. The line we want is $C + W$. The details are left to the reader. To see how these matters look in coordinates, the reader should do Exs. 1 and 2.

(4) *The points on the line joining A and B are given exactly by all*

$(1 - t)A + tB$, t *ranging over* K. Since $(1 - t)A + tB = A + t(B - A)$, we recognize $A + W$, as in (1).

This "parametric representation" is to be thought of as an affine coordinate system for the line through A and B, assigning $t = 0$ to A and $t = 1$ to B. The point $(1 - t)A + tB$ "divides the segment in the ratio $1 - t$ to t." For characteristic $\neq 2$ the point $(A + B)/2$ given by $t = \frac{1}{2}$ is especially significant, and is called the *midpoint*.

(5) Fix a vector A_0 and consider the mapping $A \to A + A_0$. It sends Π one-to-one onto itself, and sends lines into lines. We call it the *translation* by A_0. The translations form an abelian group isomorphic to V.

The introduction of translations is typical of the shift from linear algebra to affine geometry. We are giving official recognition to the fact that the origin has been divested of any special role.

(6) Linear transformations on V play a central role in the linear algebra point of view. They continue to have a place of honor geometrically. We note that a non-singular linear transformation on V induces a one-to-one mapping of Π onto itself that sends lines into lines.

(7) Next we wish to put together the thoughts in (5) and (6). We can do this in either order, and we choose rather arbitrarily to perform first a translation and then a linear transformation. Fix a vector A_0 and a non-singular linear transformation T. The mapping

$$(31) \qquad\qquad A \to A_0 + TA$$

is an *affine transformation*. It is a one-to-one mapping of Π onto itself. It preserves lines, parallelism, midpoints, and more generally the parameter t in the expression $(1 - t)A + tB$.

Let us take the time to compute a little. Given a second affine transformation based on B_0 and U we work out the product

$$A \to A_0 + TA \to B_0 + U(A_0 + TA) = (B_0 + UA_0) + UTA$$

and find it to be affine, based on $B_0 + UA_0$ and UT. The transformation based on 0 and I is the identity. There is an inverse; for the transformation (31) it is

$$A \to -T^{-1}A_0 + T^{-1}A$$

In short we have a group, the *affine group*.

We could at this point show how the formulas look in coordinates, and represent affine transformations by 3×3 matrices, but it will be more efficient to let this wait till we have embedded affine geometry into projective geometry.

(8) The reader is urged to do Exercise 3, which asserts that the translations form a normal subgroup of the affine group.

(9) We take this opportunity to mention Klein's *Erlangen* program. In a famous lecture, Felix Klein enunciated the thesis that the goal of geometry is the study of properties invariant under a particular group of transformations, the group being selected appropriately for the geometry in question.

Klein's program is widely quoted, and of considerable historical significance. But it might be a good idea to point out that geometry is not unique in possessing an *Erlangen* program. In the study of any mathematical system, the group of automorphisms is certain to be important. The classical geometries do have the feature that for them the group of automorphisms is large and reflects the properties of the geometry well.

(10) Under affine transformations, any two triangles are equivalent. For instance, let us use coordinates and move a triangle ABC to a standard position. By a translation we move A to the origin. The points B and C move to linearly independent vectors, which can be sent to $(1, 0)$ and $(0, 1)$ by a non-singular linear transformation. For uniqueness, see Ex. 10.

In the same way, any two parallelograms are affine equivalent.

(11) Suppose given a one-to-one mapping of Π onto itself that preserves lines. Must it be affine? The answer is almost "yes." The only disturbance is brought about by automorphisms of the underlying field. For fields that admit no automorphisms (prime fields, the field of real numbers) the answer is an unqualified "yes."

Two comments are in order. (a) The theorem is better done in the context of projective geometry. It is sometimes called the "fundamental theorem of projective geometry," but historically that imposing title belongs to Theorem 76. (b) The proof is moderately difficult and long. We omit it, regarding it as peripheral to an analytic presentation of geometry.

(12) It is useful to introduce affine (also called *barycentric*) coordinates in the whole plane as well as on each line. The details are set forth in Exercises 4 and 5. We shall use this technique below.

(13) Let us do some actual affine geometry. Legitimate targets are classical theorems that just mention incidence, parallelism, midpoints, or more generally, the affine parameter of division of a segment. However, theorems that mention only incidence (notably the theorems of Desargues and Pappus) belong to projective geometry and are put into storage till §3-3.

(a) *Concurrence of the medians* We start with a splendid exercise from high school geometry: prove that the three medians of a triangle are concurrent.

We have a choice of techniques. All triangles are affine equivalent, so if we know the theorem for a single triangle, all is well. We might take our triangle in a standard position: say (0, 0), (1, 0) and (0, 1), and this does simplify the computation when done in elementary style. We would rather do this exercise in a coordinate-free notation, and we shall get some practice in the use of affine coordinates while we are at it. We label the

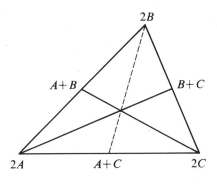

Figure 2

points as in Fig. 2, the purpose of the 2's being to avoid fractions a little. Of course for characteristic 2 there are no mid-points and the exercise is meaningless. Something peculiar also happens for characteristic 3. The vertex $2A$ is then the same as $-A$, the difference between it and $B + C$ is $A + B + C$, and this difference is the same for the three medians. So: for characteristic 3 the medians are parallel. (We feel badly the need for projective geometry, which will abolish exceptional statements of this kind).

We could finish the problem in a hurry, exhibiting the point $2(A + B + C)/3$, and verifying that it lies on all three medians. This is unimpeachable mathematics, but bad pedagogy. It is important to *discover* the formula, and we now do that.

The general point on the median joining $2A$ and $B + C$ is

(32)
$$(1 - t)2A + t(B + C)$$

and similarly we have

(33)
$$(1 - u)2C + u(A + B)$$

for the general point on the median joining $2C$ and $A + B$. To get a point of intersection we equate (32) and (33). In terms of $2A$, $2B$, and $2C$, these expressions are affine coordinates in the sense of Ex. 4. We are therefore entitled to equate coefficients of A, B, and C. We find $t = u = \frac{2}{3}$. Thus $2(A + B + C)/3$ is the point of intersection, and its symmetry shows that it lies on the remaining median.

(b) *The diagonals of a parallelogram*   According to Exercise 6, the general parallelogram is shown in Fig. 3. For characteristic 2, the diagonals are parallel. Otherwise, they meet at their common midpoint $(B + C)/2$.

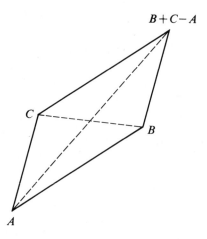

Figure 3

(c) *The theorem of Menelaus*

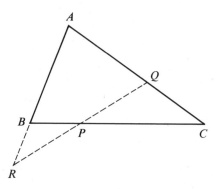

Figure 4

On the sides of the triangle with vertices A, B, C we take the points P, Q, R (Fig. 4). Say

(34)
$$P = (1 - t)B + tC$$
$$Q = (1 - u)C + uA$$
$$R = (1 - v)A + vB$$

Here t, u, $v \neq 0$ or 1, but are otherwise unrestricted. Then: P, Q, R are collinear if and only if

(35)
$$tuv = -(1 - t)(1 - u)(1 - v)$$

For the proof we cite Ex. 5 and note that the vanishing of the determinant

$$\begin{vmatrix} 0 & 1 - t & t \\ u & 0 & 1 - u \\ 1 - v & v & 0 \end{vmatrix}$$

is equivalent to (35).

Observe that no case distinctions were necessary in the discussion. But we can add them as an afterthought. If the underlying field is ordered, we can talk about the interior of the line segment joining A and B, and $(1 - t)A + tB$ lies in this interior if and only if $0 < t < 1$. Now we can see from (35) that collinearity requires that two of the points be interior and the third exterior, or else all three exterior.

(d) *The theorem of Ceva* This theorem is very similar, and the condition involved is the same as (35) except for a change of sign. We are leaving it as an exercise (7). Later we shall learn how one passes easily from one of these theorems to the other.

(e) This final item presents two affine theorems whose role will be appreciated later.

(i) We are given two triangles in perspective from 0 (Fig. 5). That is: the triangles ABC, PQR have AP, BQ, and CR all passing through 0. Assume that AB is parallel to PQ and that AC is parallel to PR. We are to prove that the third sides BC and QR are parallel.

This time we do specialize a point as origin, and naturally our choice is 0. P has the form tA for a scalar t and so (Ex. 8) $Q = tB$, $R = tC$, whence (again Ex. 8) QR is parallel to BC.

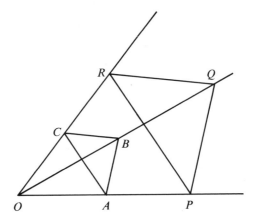

Figure 5

(*ii*) In Fig. 6, *A*, *B*, *C* are on a line and so are *P*, *Q*, *R*. We are given that *AQ* is parallel to *BP* and *CQ* parallel to *BR*. We are to prove *AR* parallel to *CP*.

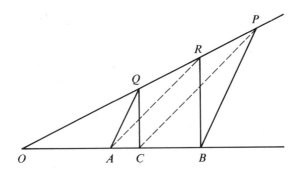

Figure 6

We take the point of intersection of the lines *ABC*, *PQR* as origin. We have, say $B = tA$, $C = uB$. Ex. 8 gives us $P = tQ$, $Q = uR$. Hence $C = utA$, $P = tuR$, *CP* is parallel to *AR*. (The alert reader may notice the switch in order of multiplication of *t* and *u* that occurred; we shall come back to this.)

EXERCISES

In Exercises 1 and 2, V is the vector space of all ordered pairs of elements of K.

1. Let p, q, $r \in K$ be given with p and q not both 0. Show that the set of all (x, y) satisfying $px + qy + r = 0$ is a line. Show that every line has this form.

2. Show that the lines given by $px + qy + r = 0$, $p_1 x + q_1 y + r_1 = 0$ are parallel or identical if and only if $pq_1 - p_1 q = 0$.

3. Show that the translations form a normal subgroup of the affine group.

4. Let A, B, C be three non-collinear points of an affine plane Π. Show that any point P of Π has an expression

$$P = tA + uB + vC$$

with $t + u + v = 1$. We call t, u, v the *affine coordinates* of P relative to A, B, C. (*Hint:* observe that $B - A$ and $C - A$ are linearly independent, and what is wanted is the unique expression of $P - A$ as a linear combination of them.)

5. Let P_i ($i = 1, 2, 3$) have affine coordinates t_i, u_i, v_i relative to three base points. Prove that P_1, P_2, P_3 are collinear if and only if the determinant

$$\begin{vmatrix} t_1 & u_1 & v_1 \\ t_2 & u_2 & v_2 \\ t_3 & u_3 & v_3 \end{vmatrix}$$

vanishes.

6. Let A, B, C be three non-collinear points. Show that the unique point D making $ABCD$ a parallelogram (AB parallel to CD, AC parallel to BD) is given by $D = B + C - A$.

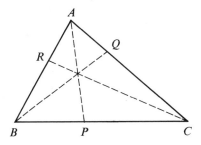

Figure 7

7. Let P, Q, R be points on the sides of the triangle ABC (Fig. 7), and assume (34). Then AP, BQ, CR are concurrent if and only if $tuv = (1 - t)(1 - u)(1 - v)$.

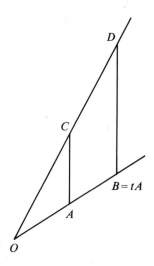

Figure 8

8. Let the points A, B, C, D be as in Fig. 8: A and $B = tA$ lie on a line through the origin, C and D on another line through the origin. Prove that BD is parallel to AC if and only if $D = tC$.

9. Given a triangle ABC (Fig. 9). Draw the line L through A parallel to BC, M

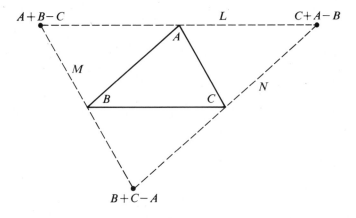

Figure 9

through B parallel to AC, and N through C parallel to AB. Prove:

(a) If the characteristic is not 2, L, M, and N form a triangle with vertices
$B + C - A$, $C + A - B$, $A + B - C$.

(b) If the characteristic is 2, prove that L, M, and N are concurrent at
$A + B + C$.

10. Let A, B, C be three points not on a line, and D, E, F another such triple. Prove that there is exactly one affine transformation carrying A into D, B into E, C into F.

11. Let Π be an affine plane over a finite field having k elements. (Note: k is a power of a prime.) Prove:

(a) There are k points on every line.

(b) There are $k + 1$ lines through every point.

(c) There are k^2 points in all.

(d) There are $k^2 + k$ lines in all.

(e) There are $k - 1$ lines parallel to a given line.

3-2   Inner Product Planes

In this section our affine plane Π acquires added structure from the presence of a non-singular inner product in the underlying two-dimensional vector space V.

One thing this gives us is the concept of orthogonality of two lines. We shall use it largely in the following form: the lines AB and CD are orthogonal if and only if $(C - A, D - B) = 0$. We shall shy away from the delicate subject of angles other than right angles.

In addition to orthogonality, we shall make use of the inner product (A,A) of a vector with itself. Keeping in mind the Euclidean case we are generalizing, we call this the square of the length (or length²) of A and write it A^2. Similarly, we write AB^2 for the length² of $B - A$ and call it the distance² from A to B. Note that we are allowing V to have null vectors, so A^2 can be 0 for $A \neq 0$.

As our first geometric illustration we discuss briefly two more of the concurrence theorems of elementary geometry.

Concurrence of the Altitudes   We are given a triangle with vertices A, B, C (Fig. 10). We draw the perpendiculars from B, C to the respective opposite sides. These altitudes cannot be parallel, for then AC and BC would be parallel. We take their point of intersection to be the origin—this streamlines the computation pleasantly. The perpendicularity of OB and AC yields

(36) $(B, C - A) = 0$

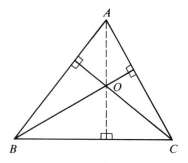

Figure 10

Similarly

(37) $(C, A - B) = 0$

Adding (36) and (37) gives us $(A, C - B) = 0$, showing that the third altitude goes through 0.

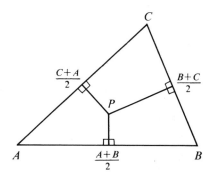

Figure 11

Concurrence of the perpendicular bisectors   We need characteristic $\neq 2$. Both methods from elementary geometry are available. We can check that P (Fig. 11) lies on the perpendicular bisector of AB if and only if $PA^2 = PB^2$. The details are that

$$(P - A, P - A) = (P - B, P - B)$$

simplifies to

$$(A,A) - 2(P,A) = (B,B) - 2(P,B)$$

which is equivalent to

$$\left(P - \frac{A + B}{2}, A - B\right) = 0$$

This is valid even if PA^2 and PB^2 are 0. Thus if two of the perpendicular bisectors meet at P, we have $PA^2 = PB^2 = PC^2$, showing P to be on the third perpendicular bisector. Or: we can pass to the triangle formed by the midpoints and argue that the perpendicular bisectors are now the three altitudes. (Actually the usual device in elementary geometry is the reverse, as in Ex. 9, page 92, since the concurrence of the altitudes is considered harder. This is fine for us too, except that we would lose the altitudes for characteristic 2.)

Would the reader like to try proving collinearity of the three points of concurrence we have found (medians, altitudes, perpendicular bisectors)?

We conclude this section by paying our respects to the group of an inner product plane. We recall that an orthogonal transformation of V is a non-singular linear transformation preserving the inner product. Next, a translation preserves the distance² between points. We combine the two thoughts. For T orthogonal, a map of the form

(38) $A \rightarrow A_0 + TA$

is called *Euclidean*. Any Euclidean mapping is affine and has the further property of preserving the distance² between points. The Euclidean transformations form a subgroup of the affine group, and we call it the Euclidean group.

Remarks 1. Any orthogonal linear transformation has determinant ± 1. By insisting on determinant 1 in (38) we can cut the group down to the *proper Euclidean group*, or *group of motions*. This is particularly pertinent over an ordered field, where we can link the determinant to the question of orienting the plane.

2. Going in the other direction we can enlarge the Euclidean group (still staying within the affine group) to the *similarity* group. For this the T in (38) is assumed to have the property $(TA,TB) = c(A,B)$ for a non-zero scalar c depending on T but not on A and B. This is the group that fits the discussion of similar geometric figures that we inherited from the Greeks.

3. Suppose we are given a one-to-one mapping of Π onto itself that preserves the distance². Is it necessarily Euclidean? (Note that a priori we do not even know it to be affine.) The answer is a firm affirmative, at least for characteristic $\neq 2$; no automorphism of the field can interfere this time. The proof is not difficult and we leave

it as a pair of exercises (2 and 3). We also leave as a project for a curious reader the discovery of what the facts are for characteristic 2.

EXERCISES

1. (The angle in a semi-circle is a right angle.) Assume characteristic $\neq 2$. Given A and B, their midpoint $C = (A + B)/2$, and a further point D (Fig. 12).

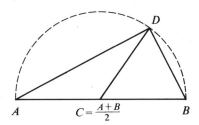

Figure 12

Show that $CA^2 = CD^2$ if and only if AD and BD are perpendicular. (*Note:* since we have not yet discussed conics, Fig. 12 shows only a "ghost" semi-circle.)

2. Let V be a non-singular inner product space of characteristic $\neq 2$. Let T be a one-to-one map of V onto itself, sending 0 into 0 and satisfying $(x,x) = (Tx,Tx)$ for all $x \in V$. Prove that T is orthogonal, i.e. it is a linear transformation and preserves inner products.

3. Let π be an inner product plane of characteristic $\neq 2$. Let T be a one-to-one map of π onto itself that preserves the distance². Prove that T is Euclidean.

4. (The diagonals of a rhombus are perpendicular.) Assume characteristic $\neq 2$ and that all sides of quadrilateral $ABCD$ have the same length² (Fig. 13). Prove that the diagonals AC and BD are perpendicular.

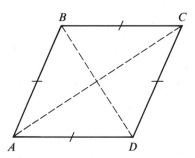

Figure 13

3-3   Projective Planes

Our motivation for the introduction of projective planes is the hope of abolishing the exceptional status of parallel lines in affine planes. It would be nice to have *every* pair of distinct lines meet in exactly one point.

Let us look at the matter from the point of view of the usual coordinates in an affine plane. We have a family of parallel lines (Fig. 14) and wish

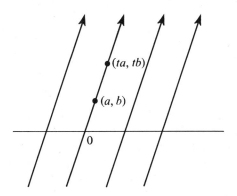

Figure 14

to assign to all of them a new point "at infinity." One of the lines goes through the origin, and the points on it are of the form (ta, tb) where t ranges over the elements of the underlying field K. What coordinates shall we give the point at infinity? We try to maintain the form (ta, tb). We get infinity when we divide by 0. So our candidate shapes up as $(a/0, b/0)$.

This, of course, is nonsense. To restore some sanity we decide to rewrite $(a/0, b/0)$ as the triple $(a, b, 0)$. No one can argue about the legitimacy of an ordered triple of elements of K; the division by 0 is now merely an intention, which we do not try to execute. To achieve uniformity, we proceed to write the ordinary (or "finite") points on the line through the origin also as triples (a, b, c) with $c \neq 0$. Here, if challenged, we actually carry out the division and restore the point to its former status $(a/c, b/c)$. Notice that for $k \neq 0$, (ka, kb, kc) will in this way give us the same point as (a, b, c). For the finite points it is true that we could normalize c to be 1, but we would then lose the possibility of treating finite and infinite points uniformly.

All this discussion could be repeated for the family of parallel lines in a second direction. And the thought is not far away of assembling all these points at infinity into a new line, the line at infinity (Fig. 15).

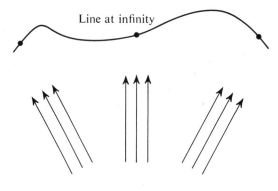

Figure 15

Let us think again of the coordinates we tentatively invented above: triples (a, b, c) where (ka, kb, kc) is regarded as the same point for $k \neq 0$. Triples are elements of a three-dimensional vector space V over K. The identification we are making amounts to collapsing a whole one-dimensional subspace of V down to a point. Without analyzing further, we announce the decision.

Definition. Let K be any field, V a three-dimensional vector space over K. V determines a projective plane Π as follows: the points of Π are the one-dimensional subspaces of V, and the lines of Π are the two-dimensional subspaces of V (each regarded as the collection of all the one-dimensional subspaces it contains).

Note. We are somewhat lazily using the same notation (V and Π) as we did in the affine case. However, when we place an affine plane inside Π, as we shall do shortly, we shall use the notation V_0 and Π_0 for the affine objects.

We note at once the two basic properties.

(1) Any two distinct points lie on a unique line. Translation into linear algebra: two distinct one-dimensional subspaces span a unique two-dimensional subspace. This statement is just the same as in the affine case.

(2) Any two distinct lines meet in exactly one point. Translation into linear algebra: in a three-dimensional vector space, two distinct two-dimensional subspaces intersect in a one-dimensional subspace. Note that, as compared with the affine case there are no exceptional parallel lines.

The foundations of the subject are so important that we shall repeat them in coordinate style. We start with a field K, and take V to be the vector space of all triples of elements of K. The associated projective plane Π has for its points the triples (a, b, c), where a, b, c are not all 0, subject to the provision that only the ratios count: for $k \neq 0$ (ka, kb, kc) is to be identified with (a, b, c). (Hence the natural name *homogeneous coordinates*.) More accurately, we should say that a point is the appropriate equivalence class of triples. Or, to revert to linear algebra, perhaps it is neatest after all to say that a point of Π is a one-dimensional subspace of V.

We turn to the lines of Π. A two-dimensional subspace of V is most easily described as the set of solutions of a linear homogeneous equation. So again we take a triple p, q, r, not all three 0; again only the ratios matter; and we get a line by assembling all the solutions (x, y, z) of the equation

$$(39) \qquad\qquad px + qy + rz = 0$$

(The fact that points and lines have emerged looking like the same equivalence classes of triples will shortly get a coordinate-free explanation.)

Next we wish to note how our previous affine plane (call it Π_0 now) sits inside Π. First: the line $z = 0$ consists of all the points at infinity; throw it away. The surviving triples (a, b, c) all have $c \neq 0$ and we are entitled to normalize them by taking $c = 1$. So: the point (a, b) of Π_0 corresponds to the point $(a, b, 1)$ of Π.

Now take a line of Π other than $z = 0$. Say the line is given by (39), and note that p and q are not both 0 (otherwise we get the discarded line $z = 0$). The affine points (x, y) lying on the line are those satisfying

$$px + qy + r = 0$$

as expected (Ex. 1 of §3-1).

Finally we note (compare Ex. 2 of §3-1) that two parallel lines of Π_0 can be put in the form

$$(40) \qquad\qquad px + qy + r = 0 \qquad px + qy + r' = 0$$

The lines of Π corresponding to (40) meet at a point at infinity; explicitly the point of intersection is $(q, -p, 0)$.

Summary. (1) The points of Π_0 are those of Π after the deletion of the points at infinity, i.e., the points on the line at infinity $z = 0$.

(2) The lines of Π_0 correspond to those of Π with the one line $z = 0$ deleted. Each line loses its point at infinity in the transition to Π.

(3) Two lines of Π_0 are parallel if and only if the corresponding lines of Π meet at a point at infinity.

Briefly and suggestively, an affine plane is a projective plane where one line has been singled out for VIP treatment. Now the beauty of this is that we are at liberty to select which line it is going to be. (We are jumping the gun slightly in anticipating that a line can be carried into any other by a projective transformation.) We are going to illustrate this trick by making the theorems of Desargues and Pappus into affine theorems.

Desargues' theorem asserts that if the lines joining corresponding vertices of two triangles are concurrent, then the intersections of corresponding pairs of sides are collinear (Fig. 16). In letters: ABC and PQR are tri-

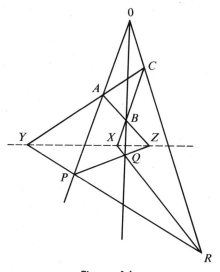

Figure 16

angles. Assume AP, BQ, CR concurrent. Let BC and QR meet at X, AC and PR at Y, AB and PQ at Z. Conclusion: X, Y, and Z lie on a line. To make this an affine theorem we choose to put the line XY at infinity. (We do not yet know Z to be on it.) Now compare with the theorem in §3-1 that was illustrated by Fig. 5.

Figure 17 illustrates Pappus' theorem. We have A, B, C on a line and P, Q, R on a second line. We form the three cross-joins: BR and QC meet at X, AR and PC meet at Y, AQ and PB meet at Z. We are to prove X, Y, Z collinear. Put XZ at infinity and you get the theorem of Fig. 6 in §3-1.

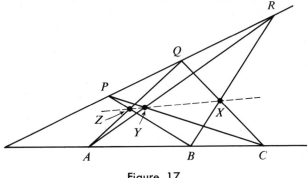

Figure 17

EXERCISES

1. (The Fano configuration) Starting with a quadrilateral *ABCD* (Fig. 18), add

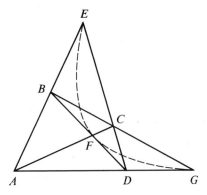

Figure 18

the additional points *E*, *F*, *G* that form the "complete quadrilateral". Prove that points *E*, *F*, *G* are always collinear if and only if the characteristic is 2.

2. In the projective plane over a finite field of k elements, prove
   (a) There are $k + 1$ points on every line and $k + 1$ lines through every point.
   (b) There are, in all, $k^2 + k + 1$ points and $k^2 + k + 1$ lines.
   (Note how simple and symmetric this is, compared with Ex. 11, page 91.)

3-4 Projective Transformations

The appropriate transformations of a projective plane arise more directly than they did in the case of affine planes. We mean by this that everything comes from linear transformations, without the need for an auxiliary type such as translations. We pay a small price, since we have to think about the way a non-singular linear transformation induces a mapping on the one-dimensional subspaces of a vector space.

We turn to the details. Let V be a three-dimensional vector space over a field K. Let T be a non-singular linear transformation on V. Then T sends every one-dimensional subspace of V onto some other one-dimensional subspace. In this way T induces a mapping of the projective plane Π into itself; let us write T_Π for the induced map. It is obvious that T_Π is one-to-one and onto. Furthermore: all the one-dimensional subspaces lying in a certain two-dimensional subspace of V are sent by T into a collection of exactly the same kind; in other words, T_Π sends lines into lines.

A one-to-one mapping of Π onto itself that sends lines into lines is called a *collineation* of Π. A mapping of the type T_Π just constructed is called by some a projective collineation or a projectivity, but we prefer the name *projective transformation*.

Any projective transformation is a collineation. Is the reverse true? Not quite. We repeat the remarks made in §3-1.

(1) There is a moderately hard theorem involved and we are omitting it.

(2) A collineation is more general than a projective transformation, exactly to the extent that automorphisms of the underlying field are involved.

How much freedom of motion do we have in a projective transformation? The answer is gratifyingly simple: given any four points of Π, no three of them on a line, there is a unique projective transformation sending them into any other such quadruple. We state this in detail in Theorems 72 and 73. (These are the first assertions in Chapter 3 to be elevated to the rank of theorems!) We wish to remind the reader that we are still doing linear algebra, so we retreat momentarily from the geometric language.

Theorem 72. Let V be a three-dimensional vector space over a field K. Let A, B, C, D be one-dimensional subspaces of V, no three of them lying in a two-dimensional subspace. Let E, F, G, H be another such quadruple. Then there exists a non-singular linear transformation of V carrying A, B, C, D (in that order) into E, F, G, H.

Proof. In this proof, and on several later occasions, we adopt the following convention: when we pick a particular representative (non-zero, of course) of a one-dimensional subspace, we use the corresponding small Greek letter, e.g. $\alpha, \beta, \gamma, \delta$ in A, B, C, D. As a geometer would say, we are fixing the homogeneous coordinates of these points.

We can simplify our task somewhat by working with a standard quadruple. If we show that the standard quadruple can be sent into an arbitrary quadruple, then by doing this twice (and inverting one of the transformations) we get our theorem. The selected quadruple will be $\epsilon_1 = (1, 0, 0)$, $\epsilon_2 = (0, 1, 0)$, $\epsilon_3 = (0, 0, 1)$, $\epsilon_4 = (1, 1, 1)$.

Our hypothesis that A, B, C are not in a two-dimensional subspace says that α, β, γ are linearly independent. Hence we may write $\delta = a\alpha + b\beta + c\gamma$ $(a,b, c \in K)$. All of the coefficients a, b, c must be non-zero, or we again violate our hypothesis that no three of A, B, C, D are in the same two-dimensional subspace. We define T by $T\epsilon_1 = a\alpha$, $T\epsilon_2 = b\beta$, $T\epsilon_3 = c\gamma$. Then T is non-singular, satisfies $T\epsilon_4 = \delta$, and thus fulfills our requirements.

We turn to the uniqueness of the linear transformation obtained in Theorem 72. Two remarks are in order: (1) We can reduce the uniqueness problem to the case where T keeps a quadruple fixed; (2) After this is done, we cannot hope to prove T to be the identity, for a (non-zero) scalar multiple of the identity is just as good.

Theorem 73. *Let V be a three-dimensional vector space over a field K. Let A, B, C, D be one-dimensional subspaces, no three of which lie in a two-dimensional subspace. Let T be a non-singular linear transformation on V, sending A, B, C, D into themselves. Then T is a scalar multiple of the identity.*

Proof. By Theorem 72 we can take A, B, C, D to be represented by the vectors ϵ_i $(i = 1, \cdots, 4)$ that were used in its proof. Then we have $T\epsilon_i = c_i\epsilon_i$ for scalars c_i. In matrix terms, the first three of these equations say that T is a diagonal matrix with c_1, c_2, c_3 down the diagonal. The remaining equation $T\epsilon_4 = c_4\epsilon_4$ forces $c_1 = c_2 = c_3$.

Two further remarks will conclude this section.

1. The *projective group* is the group of all projective transformations of Π. It is the full linear group (group of all non-singular linear transformations) on V, modulo the non-zero scalars.

2. Here is how the affine group fits in. For a projective transformation to induce an affine one, it has to leave the line at infinity fixed (not pointwise but as a whole). Putting this in matrix terms, we work out the form of such a linear transformation as

$$\begin{pmatrix} a & b & c \\ d & e & f \\ 0 & 0 & 1 \end{pmatrix}$$

where we have normalized the lower right entry to be 1. The 2×2 upper left corner gives the linear transformation part of the affine transformation, and the vector (c, f) names the translation.

EXERCISES

1. Prove that any affine transformation of an affine plane Π_0 extends uniquely to a projective transformation of the corresponding projective plane Π.
2. (Continuation of 1) (a) If the affine transformation is a translation, prove that the projective transformation leaves every point at infinity fixed.
   (b) Investigate conversely the affine nature of a projective transformation that leaves every point at infinity fixed.

3-5 Duality

We shall show how duality in vector spaces gives rise to a very convincing duality in projective planes.

Let V be an n-dimensional vector space over a field K. Let V^* be the dual space. We recall how a correspondence is established between the subspaces of V and those of V^*. For any subspace S of V, we take the subspace of V^* consisting of all linear functions vanishing on S. Notice that this is quite analogous to the orthogonal complement in an inner product space; we use the same notation, S'. If S is r-dimensional, S' is $(n - r)$-dimensional, and we have $S'' = S$. Since V is also the dual of V^*, the correspondence works both ways, and in fact is one-to-one and onto between all of the subspaces of V and all those of V^*.

Now take $n = 3$. The one-dimensional subspaces of V constitute the projective plane Π, and those of V^* form a second projective plane Π^*. The mapping described above sends the points of Π into the lines of Π^*, and the lines of Π into the points of Π^*. Such a mapping between projective planes is called a *correlation*. In sum: there is a natural correlation between Π and the dual plane Π^*.

The reader may object that all this accomplishes very little, for V and V^* are really the same vector space, and so Π and Π^* are the same projective plane. We offer two answers. First: in §3-9, where we allow K to be noncommutative, we shall find that Π^* can be different from Π. Second (and more important): we have established the principal of duality for projective planes. *Any theorem on projective planes remains a true theorem* (and needs no further proof!) *if points and lines are interchanged.* In the exercises we invite the reader to experiment on three theorems.

EXERCISES

1. Dualize Desargues' theorem. How is the dual related to the theorem?
2. Dualize Pappus' theorem. Draw a figure to illustrate the dual.
3. Show that the Fano theorem for characteristic 2 (Ex. 1, page 101) is self-dual.

3-6 Cross Ratio and Harmonic Range

In the initial part of this section we retreat from two-dimensional projective geometry to the one-dimensional case. One might expect that everything to be said is analogous and easier. This is true in part, but the considerations that lead us to cross ratio were not treated above.

Once again we formulate the basic result as a piece of linear algebra. Theorem 74 is a splendid example of the transition from algebra to geometry; it is a nice exercise in linear algebra, but utterly artificial without the geometric motivation.

Theorem 74. Let A, B, C, D be distinct one-dimensional subspaces of a two-dimensional vector space V over a field K. Then we can find non-zero vectors $\alpha, \beta, \gamma, \delta$ in A, B, C, D respectively, in such a way that $\gamma = \alpha + \beta$, $\delta = k\alpha + \beta, k \in K$. The number k is independent of the way the selection is made, and it is different from 0 and 1.

Proof. Take provisional representatives α, β of A and B. Necessarily α and β span V (A and B are distinct). When γ is written as a linear combination of α and β, both coefficients must be non-zero, for otherwise C would coincide with A or B. By changing our minds about α and β we can achieve $\gamma = \alpha + \beta$. Similarly δ is a linear combination of α and β with both coefficients non-zero. This time we change δ by a scalar factor to make the coefficient of β equal to 1, and then $\delta = k\alpha + \beta$. Of course $k \neq 0, 1$.

Suppose the procedure is done a second time, yielding vectors $\alpha_0, \beta_0, \gamma_0, \delta_0$. Say $\alpha_0 = r\alpha, \beta_0 = s\beta$. We have $\gamma_0 = r\alpha + s\beta$ and this must be a scalar multiple of $\gamma = \alpha + \beta$. Hence $r = s$. If $\delta_0 = k_0\alpha_0 + \beta_0$ we have $\delta_0 = r(k_0\alpha + \beta)$, which is a multiple of $k\alpha + \beta$ only if $k_0 = k$.

Remarks. 1. What we have achieved may be looked at as a coordinate system for the projective line in question. As k runs over K, $k\alpha + \beta$ gives us all points on the line except A, which, reasonably enough, gets awarded the coordinate ∞. So the coordinate system is describable as follows: three base points are selected and get coordinates 0, 1, ∞ ; the remaining elements of K fill out the rest of the line.

2. If K is a very small field, the effect on Theorem 74 is somewhat bizarre. For the field of two elements, the entire setup of Theorem 74 is impossible. For the field of three elements, we can forget about the uniqueness of k, since it has to be -1.

We wish to record the one-dimensional analogues of Theorems 72 and 73, but shall not repeat the proofs. It might be noted that we could state Theorems 75 and 76 in a strictly one-dimensional form, but it fits our context better to formulate them for a projective line embedded in a projective plane.

Theorem 75. *Let A, B, C be three distinct collinear points in a projective plane* Π, *and let D, E, F be another such triple. Then there exists a projective transformation of* Π *sending A into D, B into E, C into F.*

The linear transformation constructed in Theorem 75 is unique on the rest of the line. We state this after the usual normalization.

Theorem 76. *Let A, B, C be distinct points on a line L of a projective plane* Π. *If a projective transformation of* Π *leaves A, B, and C fixed, then it leaves every point of L fixed.*

We return to Theorem 74. The procedure has attached to the ordered quadruple A, B, C, D an element of K. We call it the *cross ratio* and write it $(ABCD)$. The definition makes Theorem 77 apparent.

Theorem 77. *Cross ratio is invariant under a projective transformation.*

We proceed to prove that cross ratio is invariant under perspective from a point (Fig. 19).

Theorem 78. *Let A, B, C, D be four distinct points on a line of a projective plane. Let A', B', C', D' be another such quadruple. Suppose AA', BB', CC', DD' all meet at E. Then the cross ratios $(ABCD)$ and $(A'B'C'D')$ are equal.*

Proof. We assign coordinates to A, B, C, D as in Theorem 74: α, β, $\alpha + \beta$, $k\alpha + \beta$. Let ϵ represent E. For A' we can pick a representative of the form $\alpha + t\epsilon$, and similarly $\beta + u\epsilon$ for B'. Now we examine $(\alpha + \beta) +$

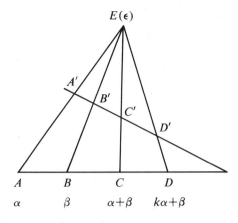

Figure 19

$(t + u)\epsilon$. In this form we recognize it as being on the line CE. In the form $(\alpha + t\epsilon) + (\beta + u\epsilon)$ we see that it is on $A'B'$. Hence it is a vector representing C'. Likewise $k(\alpha + t\epsilon) + (\beta + u\epsilon)$ represents D'. The coordinates we have assigned identify k as the cross ratio $(A'B'C'D')$.

Given four distinct lines through a point (geometers call this a *pencil*), Theorem 78 gives us a well-defined way of defining a cross ratio for them: cut the lines with a transversal and take the cross ratio of the four resulting points; Theorem 78 shows that the result does not depend on the choice of transversal.

This, however, reminds us of duality (§3-5). For Π we have a dual plane Π^* and a mapping of Π into Π^* that sends points into lines and lines into points. This gives us another way to define the cross ratio of four concurrent lines. As an unofficial exercise for the reader we suggest that he verify that the two definitions are identical.

Let us derive the classical formula for cross ratio. For this purpose we think of four points on the x-axis of a coordinatized affine plane. In projective style, the points will be as specified in Theorem 79.

Theorem 79. Let A, B, C, D *be given by* $(a, 0, 1)$, $(b, 0, 1)$, $(c, 0, 1)$ *and* $(d, 0, 1)$, *where* a, b, c, d *are distinct elements of* K. *Then*

(41) $$'(ABCD) = \frac{(c - a)(d - b)}{(c - b)(d - a)}$$

Proof. We seek multiples *r*, *s* so that

(42) $$(c, 0, 1) = r(a, 0, 1) + s(b, 0, 1)$$

From (41) we get the equations

$$r + s = 1 \qquad ra + sb = c$$

which we solve:

$$r = \frac{c - b}{a - b} \qquad s = \frac{c - a}{b - a}$$

Similarly we set

$$(d, 0, 1) = u(a, 0, 1) + v(b, 0, 1)$$

and get

$$u = \frac{d - b}{a - b} \qquad v = \frac{d - a}{b - a}$$

To have *D* in the required form, we write

(43) $$\frac{s}{v}(d, 0, 1) = \frac{su}{rv} r(a, 0, 1) + s(b, 0, 1)$$

and from (43) we recognize (*ABCD*) to be *su/rv*, which, written in full, is the expression in (41).

We have perhaps not emphasized sufficiently that cross ratio is a number attached to an *ordered* quadruple of distinct collinear points. What happens if we permute the points?

Theorem 80. (*ABCD*) = (*BADC*) = (*CDAB*) = (*DCBA*).

Proof. We can prove this by brutally testing it on formula (41). An alternative is a pretty, synthetic proof based on a repeated use of Theorem 78. With the points as in Fig. 20 we have the chain of equations:

$$(ABCD) \overset{P}{=} (QSRD) \overset{A}{=} (PTRC) \overset{S}{=} (BADC)$$

where the letter above the equality sign indicates the point from which the perspective is taken. This shows that we can interchange simultaneously

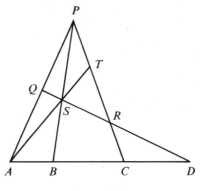

Figure 20

A, *B* and *C*, *D*. By symmetry the other two permutations in the theorem follow.

Remarks. 1. By testing reasonably random numbers in (41) we can see that no other permutations leave the cross ratio invariant. See also Exs. 1 and 2.

2. A little group theory helps to explain what is going on. The full group of permutations on four points is the symmetric group S_4. Theorem 80, together with the remark just made, says that the subgroup leaving cross ratio invariant is Klein's four-group V. Left to act effectively is S_4/V, which happens to be isomorphic to S_3.

We reluctantly abandon characteristic 2, and say that *A*, *B*, *C*, *D* form a *harmonic range* if $(ABCD) = -1$. (Why pick on -1? Because after the prohibited elements 0 and 1, the most important element in K is surely -1.) In this case, in addition to the permutations permitted in Theorem 80, we can interchange *A* and *B* or *C* and *D* separately (check by (41), or use Ex. 1). So we might say instead that the pair *A*, *B* is harmonic relative to the pair *C*, *D*.

We prove at once that the concept of harmonic range can be identified with the affine concept of midpoint.

Theorem 81. Let *A*, *B*, *C*, *D* be four distinct points on a line of a coordinatized projective plane of characteristic $\neq 2$. Suppose *A* is at infinity, and *B*, *C*, *D* are affine. Then *A*, *B*, *C*, *D* form a harmonic range if and only if *B* is the midpoint of *CD*.

Proof. We take our points in the standard form α, β, $\alpha + \beta$, $k\alpha + \beta$. Let $\alpha = (a, b, 0)$. We can take β in the form $(c, d, 1)$. (Still further normalization is possible but hardly worthwhile.)

In affine coordinates we have

$$B = (c, d) \qquad C = (a + c, b + d) \qquad D = (ka + c, ka + d)$$

Obviously B is the midpoint of CD if and only if $k = -1$.

There is a classical construction for a fourth point to complete a harmonic range. In Fig. 21, the points A, B, C are given. An auxiliary point P

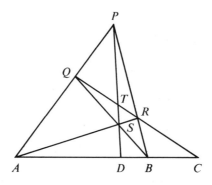

Figure 21

is selected at random, and also an auxiliary line through C meeting AP at Q and BP at R. AR and BQ meet at S, and PS meets ABC in the desired point D.

We shall prove that A, B, C, D form a harmonic range by the trick of making the problem affine. We select PSD to be the line at infinity. Then $ARBQ$ becomes a parallelogram (Fig. 22). The diagonals bisect each other and so C is the midpoint of AB.

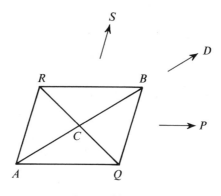

Figure 22

Suggestion. The reader might enjoy seeing what happens to Fig. 21 if other lines are placed at infinity (*PC, PQA*, etc.).

While we have Fig. 21 in front of us, let us redeem the promise made in §3-1 to demonstrate a connection between the theorems of Menelaus and Ceva. Think of *PAB* as the given triangle, with *Q, R* given on the sides *PA, PB*. If we look for a third point collinear with *Q, R* we get *C*. If instead we want a third line concurrent with *AR* and *BQ* we are led to *D*. So the two points that arise make a harmonic range together with *A* and *B*. This explains the formulas, which were identical except for sign; we invite the reader to check details. (Remark: Ex. 6 is pertinent).

The reader should also compare Fig. 21 with the Fano configuration (Ex. 1, page 101) and see the connection with the equation $-1 = 1$.

As a second illustration of the interplay between the concepts of harmonic range and midpoint we show the reader the projective version of the theorem on the concurrence of the medians. In Fig. 23, *ABC* is the given triangle, *DEF* is playing the role of the line at infinity. Hypothesis:

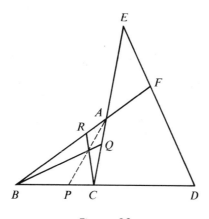

Figure 23

BCPD, CAQE, ABRF are harmonic ranges. Conclusion: *AP, BQ, CR* meet at a point.

We conclude this section by investigating briefly what it means projectively for an affine plane Π_0 to be an inner product plane (§3-2). We do this on the assumption that the characteristic is not 2 and that the underlying inner product space (call it V_0) is isotropic, i.e. a hyperbolic plane. We recall (Ex. 12, page 21) that V_0 has exactly two isotropic one-dimensional subspaces. Switching to the geometric language we say that there are two isotropic (self-perpendicular) lines through the origin. Similarly there are two isotropic lines through any point of Π_0.

> *Theorem 80.* *Let V_0 be a hyperbolic plane over a field K of characteristic $\neq 2$. Let Π_0 be the corresponding inner product plane. Let L, M be any lines of Π_0 meeting, say, in P. Let L_1, M_1 be the isotropic lines through P. Then: L_1, M_1, L, M form a harmonic pencil if and only if L and M are perpendicular.*

Proof. We may take P to be the origin. Then points on the four lines can be taken as in Theorem 74: α on L_1, β on M_1, $\alpha + \beta$ on L, $k\alpha + \beta$ on M. We have $0 = (\alpha,\alpha) = (\beta,\beta)$, and say $(\alpha,\beta) = r$. We find $(\alpha + \beta, k\alpha + \beta) = (k + 1)r$, which is 0 if and only if $k = -1$.

Let us make a connection with the projective plane in which Π_0 is embedded. The isotropic lines of Π_0 fall into two parallel families; these meet the line at infinity at two points, which we denote by I and J. Tradition decrees that we call I and J the *circular points at infinity.*

We recapitulate the projective description of perpendicularity that we have achieved: given L and M meeting at P, join P to I and J; for perpendicularity the four lines L, M, PI, PJ have to form a harmonic pencil (Fig. 24).

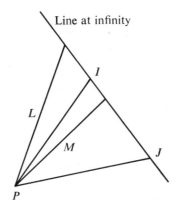

Line at infinity

I

L

M

J

P

I, J circular points at infinity
Pencil harmonic $\leftrightarrow$ L, M perpendicular

Figure 24

Summary: to pass from harmonic ranges to midpoints, you distinguish one line and call it the line at infinity. To pass from harmonic ranges to perpendicularity, you further distinguish two points on the line at infinity.

One final comment is in order. Our discussion does not fit the most important example of all, the Euclidean plane, because its inner product is positive definite. The answer is to enlarge the field to the complex numbers. In the usual coordinate system, I and J get the coordinates $(1, i, 0)$ and $(1, -i, 0)$ where $i^2 = -1$.

Our ancestors showed considerable courage in introducing the circular points at infinity, points that are ghostly for two reasons: they are at infinity and they are imaginary.

EXERCISES

1. If $(ABCD) = k$, prove that $(BACD) = k^{-1}$ and $(ACBD) = 1 - k$.

2. Show that in general one gets 6 different cross ratios on permuting

$$k, k^{-1}, 1 - k, (k - 1)k^{-1}, (1 - k)^{-1}, \text{ and } k(k - 1)^{-1}$$

3. If A, B, C, D form a harmonic range and have coordinates as in Theorem 79, prove

$$\frac{2}{b - a} = \frac{1}{c - a} + \frac{1}{d - a}$$

4. Restate the theorem of the concurrence of the three altitudes of a triangle as a projective theorem.

5. Let A, B, C, D be four distinct collinear points in a coordinatized projective plane. Assume that A is at infinity, B, C, and D are affine, and $D = (1 - k)B + kC$. Prove that $(ABCD) = k$. (*Hint:* the notation used in the proof of Theorem 81 is applicable.)

6. In affine coordinates let $C = (1 - t)A + tB$, $D = (1 - k)A + kB$. Prove that $(ABCD) = t(k - 1)/k(t - 1)$.

7. Discuss the theorem of Fig. 23 in projective style. (*Hint:* show that RQD, PQF, PRE are each on a line.)

3-7   Conics

The material we present in this section is to a large extent a translation of numerous small results on inner product spaces to the geometric language.

(1) *Setup* K is a field of characteristic $\neq 2$, V a three-dimensional vector space over K, Π the associated projective plane. We now assume that V is an inner product space. We cheerfully and instantly bypass a point that looms large in elementary discussions by assuming the form non-singular.

(2) *The conic*   In coordinate style we have a homogeneous equation of the second degree in three variables. The conic Γ is the set of all points of Π satisfying this equation, the homogeneity assuring us that this makes sense. Translation back to linear algebra: Γ is the set of all isotropic one-dimensional subspaces of V.

(3) *All conics are the same*   If the form is non-isotropic, there is no conic. So we assume at least one null vector and then have at least one point on Γ. As a consequence there are lots of points on Γ. (Modest exercise: if K is infinite, then Γ is infinite.)

It is harmless to multiply the form by a non-zero constant c. This will multiply the discriminant by c^3, or by c (since we ignore squares). We take advantage of this normalization to make the discriminant -1. Then (Ex. 3 in §1-8) the form can be diagonalized with diagonal entries $1, 1, -1$. In coordinate style, our normalized conic is $x^2 + y^2 - z^2 = 0$.

Note that all this is valid for arbitrary K, subject only to the assumption that the form is isotropic. Of course, if every element in K is a square, no assumption is needed.

(4) *Intersection of a line and a conic*   A line L of Π corresponds to a two-dimensional subspace S of V. There are three possibilities: (a) S is non-singular and non-isotropic (L does not meet Γ); (b) S is non-singular and isotropic (L meets Γ in two points); (c) S is singular, necessarily with a one-dimensional radical. In this last case L meets Γ in one point, and we call L a *tangent* to Γ.

(5) *Pole and polar*   The taking of orthogonal complements bounces us back and forth between one-dimensional and two-dimensional subspaces. Geometrically we talk about the *polar* of a point, the *pole* of a line.

(6) *Tangent line at a point*   If P lies on Γ there is a unique tangent to Γ through P, namely the polar of P. (If W is an isotropic one-dimensional subspace of V, the only singular two-dimensional subspace containing W is the orthogonal complement W'.)

(7) *Conjugate points*   Points corresponding to orthogonal one-dimensional subspaces are called conjugate.

(8) *Geometric construction of pole and polar*   If a line L meets Γ at A and B, and the tangents at A and B meet at P, then P is the pole of L (Fig. 25). For P is conjugate to both A and B and therefore AB is the polar of L.

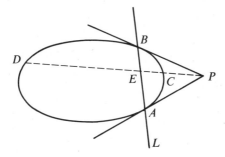

Figure 25

(9) *A harmonic range*   In Fig. 25 draw another line through *P*, meeting Γ at *C* and *D*, and meeting *L* at *E*. Then: *PECD* is a harmonic range. We need only apply Theorem 80 to the two-dimensional subspace of *V* corresponding to this new line.

(10) *Affine versions*   Write L_∞ for the line at infinity. Γ is an *ellipse* if L_∞ does not meet Γ, a *hyperbola* if L_∞ meets Γ in two points, a *parabola* if L_∞ is tangent to Γ.

The reader should try the experiment of putting various lines at infinity in Fig. 25.

(11) *Circles*   With a minimum of discussion we assert that a circle is a conic through the two circular points at infinity. One of the most exciting aspects of the development of projective geometry was the discovery that the myriads of special properties possessed by circles were simply general properties of conics relative to two distinguished points.

For variety, let us move a theorem from Euclidean to projective geometry. We select the theorem that the angle in a semi-circle is a right angle (Fig. 26; compare the discussion with Ex. 1, page 96). In making the

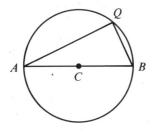

Figure 26

transition we note that the center of any conic is the pole of the line at infinity (exercise!). The result is the assertion in Fig. 27 that the pencil

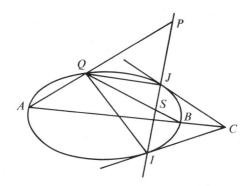

Figure 27

QA, QB, QI, QJ is harmonic. Now there is no doubt that our deliberations add up to a proof of this projective theorem. Nevertheless we shall give a proof in projective style (essentially the one in [9]); it is a little harder than one might expect.

We return to Fig. 21, the geometric construction for a harmonic range. Suppose the points A, Q, R, B lie on a conic Γ. Then we assert that $PTSD$ is the polar of C. For we have that $CDBA$ is a harmonic range. By the theorem of Fig. 25, D lies on the polar of C. The same argument shows that T is on the polar of C, and we thus identify DT as the polar of C, as stated. The points P, S, C (the diagonal points of the quadrilateral inscribed in the conic) play a symmetric role, so we actually get that PSC is a *self-polar triangle;* each side is the polar of the opposite vertex.

Now return to Fig. 27. Let QA meet IJ at P, and QB meet IJ at S. Our problem is to prove $IJSP$ a harmonic range. Just keeping the six points A, Q, P, S, B, C (ignore I, J and the conic), completes Fig. 21. The harmonic range properties of Fig. 21 show D to be the intersection of IJ and CA in Fig. 27, and show further that R lies on the conic. Therefore our argument above applies, to show that CSP is self-polar. In particular, P and S are conjugate, and hence $IJSP$ is a harmonic range.

Before leaving this circle of ideas, let us make one more translation from geometry into linear algebra, namely the theorem of the self-polar triangle just demonstrated and used. The result is rather striking. Theorem: let A, B, C, D be distinct one-dimensional isotropic subspaces of a three-dimensional non-singular inner product space of characteristic $\neq 2$. Use the notation $\{A,B\}$ for the subspace spanned by A and B. Then the one-dimensional subspaces

$$\{A,B\}\cap\{C,D\}   \{A,C\}\cap\{B,D\}   \{A,D\}\cap\{B,C\}$$

are orthogonal.

(12) *Steiner's theorem*   Let A, B, C, D be four fixed points on a conic Γ, P a variable point on Γ. Then the cross ratio of the pencil PA, PB, PC, PD is independent of P (Fig. 28).

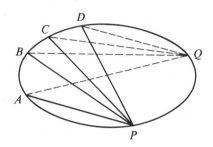

Figure 28

We prove this by a direct computation, taking advantage of a suitable basis. We can have A, B, C, D represented by

$$\alpha = (1,0,0),\ \beta = (0,1,0),\ \gamma = (0,0,1),\ \delta = (1,1,1).$$

Suppose $(\alpha,\beta) = c$, $(\alpha,\gamma) = b$, $(\beta,\gamma) = a$. Note that α, β, γ, δ are all isotropic. The equation $(\delta,\delta) = 0$ gives us

(44) $$a + b + c = 0$$

Let P be (u, v, w). Since P lies on Γ we get

(45) $$avw + bwu + cuv = 0$$

To make the computation of cross ratio we work on the line AB. We find the intersection of PC and AB to be $(u, v, 0)$; the intersection of PD and AB is $(u - w, v - w, 0)$. We line up our four points as

$$(u, 0, 0)$$
$$(0, v, 0)$$
$$(u, v, 0)$$
$$\frac{v(u - w)}{u(v - w)}(u, 0, 0) + (0, v, 0)$$

and recognize the cross ratio as

(46)
$$\frac{v(u - w)}{u(v - w)}$$

From (44) we have $c = -a - b$. Substitute this in (45). The result is

(47) $a(vw - uv) + b(wu - uv) = 0.$

Equation (47) shows that (46) equals $-b/a$, proving it to be independent of u, v, w, as required.

Steiner's theorem allows us to speak unambiguously of the cross ratio of four points on a conic, and we do so in proving Pascal's theorem.

(13) *Pascal's theorem*   Let A, B, C, P, Q, R be six distinct points on a conic. Let QC and BR meet at X, PC and AR at Y, and PB and AQ at Z. Then X, Y, and Z are collinear (Fig. 29).

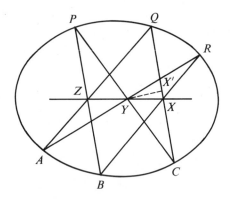

Figure 29

There exists a pleasant synthetic proof. Let ZY meet BR at X', PYC meet BR at T, PZB meet AYR at S. Then $(BTXR) \overset{C}{=} (BPQR) \overset{A}{=} (BPZS) \overset{Y}{=} (BTX'R)$. Hence $X = X'$.

If we admit two lines as a degenerate case of a conic, we can regard Pappus' theorem as a special case of Pascal's theorem.

(14) *Duality*   Let V^* be the dual of V. The form on V induces an iso-morphism of V onto V^*. Via this isomorphism we move the form over to a

form on V^*. Thus for the conic Γ in the projective plane Π, we get a dual conic Γ^* in Π^*. In the correlation between Π and Π^* it turns out that a point of Γ goes into a tangent line to Γ^*. This shows us how to dualize theorems on conics.

In particular, the dual of Pascal's theorem is shown in Fig. 30: given a hexagon circumscribed about a circle, the three "long" diagonals are concurrent. (We have used small letters for lines corresponding to capital letters used for points in Fig. 29).

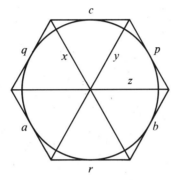

Figure 30

This dual is called *Brianchon's theorem*. As the name shows, it took some time till our ancestors recognized the two theorems as being essentially identical.

EXERCISES

1. Let A, B, C, D be four distinct points on a conic, and let L be the tangent at A. Prove: $(A, B, C, D) = (L, AB, AC, AD)$. (This is the "limiting case" of Steiner's theorem, where two of the five points coincide. Over the real field we could get it by a continuity argument. The algebraic geometers can show us how to mimic this algebraically. But it is simple enough to compute it out. Using the notation above for Steiner's theorem we already have $(ABCD) = -b/a$.)

2. Let A, B, C, P, R be five distinct points on a conic, and let L be the tangent at A. Suppose AC and BR meet at X, PC and AR at Y, and PB and L at X. Prove that X, Y, Z are concurrent. (This is Pascal's theorem with Q and A collapsed. Adapt the proof, with the aid of Ex. 1.)

3. Let five points be given, no three of them on a line. Prove that there is a unique conic through them.

4. Let a conic Γ be given in an affine plane. Prove that the midpoints of a family of parallel chords lie on a line through the center of Γ. (Make the proposition projective and compare with Fig. 25, page 115.)

5. Let A, D, C be points on a parabola, with DC parallel to the tangent at A. Let E be the midpoint of DC. Prove that AE is parallel to the axis of the parabola. (Put PB at infinity in Fig. 25.)

6. Let the tangents at points I, J on a conic meet at C. Let another line through C meet the conic at A and B. Let L be the tangent at A. Prove that the pencil L, AB, AI, AJ is harmonic. (This is the theorem of Fig. 27, page 116, with Q collapsed to A. The proof is easier. Let L meet IJ at T and AB meet IJ at S. Then T is on the polar of C, so C is on the polar of T, and so is A; then AC is the polar of T. Use the theorem of Fig. 25.)

7. In Ex. 6, take I and J to be the circular points at infinity. What Euclidean theorem do you get?

3-8   Higher Dimensional Spaces

We survey higher dimensional spaces under several subheadings.

(1) *Affine spaces*   We allow V to be any vector space over a field K, even infinite-dimensional. Looked at as an affine space, it has the very same points. But the affine subspaces are not only the vector subspaces but their cosets. A good name to use is "flat." So: a *flat* is a coset of a subspace; its dimension is that of the subspace of which it is a coset. The intersection of any number of flats is a flat. Thus there is a smallest flat generated by any subset of V. Points $P_1, \cdots, P_{n+1}$ are *affine independent* if they span an n-dimensional flat F; the points of F are given by $\Sigma\, a_i P_i$ with $\Sigma\, a_i = 1$. If K is an ordered field we get the n-simplex spanned by $P_1, \cdots, P_{n+1}$ by restricting the a_i's to be non-negative.

Remark. The affine combination $\Sigma\, a_i P_i$ can be regarded as the fundamental operation for an "origin-free" treatment of affine geometry. For a careful discussion along these lines, Chapter 12 of [28] is highly recommended.

The phenomenon of parallelism prevents us from making comprehensive statements about when two flats intersect. But we can say this: if an r-flat and an s-flat lie in an n-flat with $n < r + s$, and if they intersect at all, then their intersection has dimension $r + s - n$.

(2) *Projective spaces*   Again V is any vector space. The attached projective space Π has for its points the one-dimensional subspaces of V. The

projective subspaces of Π are simply the subspaces of V (no cosets this time!) but perhaps "flat" is still a good name.

If V is $(n + 1)$-dimensional, we say that Π is n-dimensional. If $r + s \geqq n$, an r-flat and an s-flat in Π will intersect in an $(r + s - n)$-flat.

A *hyperplane* is a flat whose dimension is one less than that of the space. An affine space is obtained from a projective space of the same dimension by deleting a hyperplane, which we call the hyperplane at infinity.

(3) *Duality* With V finite-dimensional there is a dual Π^* to go along with Π. The correlation between Π and Π^* interchanges points and hyperplanes. If the dimension of Π is n, the duality interchanges r-flats and s-flats, with $r + s = n - 1$.

When V and Π are infinite-dimensional, duality runs into trouble, and the whole matter needs reconsideration in a way that is beyond the scope of this book.

(4) *Quadrics* As soon as the dimension of V exceeds 3, we lose the simplicity that we observed in the case of conics. There may be lots of distinct quadrics, and the number depends in a complicated way on the nature of the field K, the problem being almost the same as the classification of inner product spaces over K. Of course if K is closed under square roots, there is only one form and only one quadric. When K is real closed, the number of distinct quadrics is $[n/2]$, where n is the dimension of V. For instance, when $n = 4$ (projective three-space) there are two quadrics. The ellipsoid and hyperboloid of two sheets are affinely distinct but projectively identical. The hyperboloid of one sheet is however quite a different object, even projectively; for instance, unlike the other kind of quadric it contains entire lines. (Linear algebra version of this statement: the inner product space in question contains a two-dimensional totally isotropic subspace, or equivalently, two orthogonal hyperbolic planes.)

Remarks. 1. In the above discussion, as in §3–7, we have set aside the singular quadrics (cones and cylinders). Filling in the details here would be a good exercise for the reader.

2. We have also, again as in §3–7, ignored non-isotropic inner products (quadrics with no points). This deserves reconsideration, and should be viewed in the general context of algebraic varieties. But it is beyond the scope of our treatment.

3. By orthogonal complementation we get the analogue of poles and polars. In particular we have such a pairing for points and hyperplanes.

Taking the affine point of view, we call the pole of the hyperplane at infinity the *center* of the quadric, and we call the quadric *central* if its center is not at infinity.

The following table gives concisely the five main classification problems for a non-singular quadric in n-dimensional projective space, and their linear algebra versions.

Classification of Non-Singular Quadrics in n-Space

geometric problems	algebraic version
1. Projective classification	1. Equivalence of $(n + 1)$-dimensional inner product spaces under "homothety," i.e. f is identified with cf for $c \neq 0$.
2. Affine classification of central quadrics	2. Equivalence of n-dimensional forms
3. Euclidean classification of central quadrics	3. n-dimensional self-adjoint linear transformations under orthogonal similarity
4. Affine classification of non-central quadrics	4. Equivalence of $(n - 1)$-dimensional forms under homothety
5. Euclidean classification of non-central quadrics	5. Orthogonal similarity of $(n-1)$-dimensional self-adjoint linear transformations, T being identified with $-T$.

We leave it to the interested reader to supply the details of the translation.

(5) *Embedding of Euclidean geometry*   The setup we have to examine is the following: we have V and its projective space Π, and the affine spaces V_0 and Π_0 obtained by deleting H, the hyperplane at infinity. Now suppose there is an inner product on V_0. The lines that are isotropic relative to this inner product cut out a quadric in H, which carries all the essential features of the inner product geometry in Π_0. Note that the two circular points at infinity we previously encountered form a zero-dimensional quadric. In the actual Euclidean case (a positive definite form over a real-closed field), the quadric at infinity is imaginary, and has to be brought to life by complexifying.

EXERCISE

Let Π be an n-dimensional projective space, and P_0, P_1, $\cdots$, P_n points no n of which lie in an $(n - 1)$-flat. Let $Q_0, Q_1, \cdots, Q_n$ be another such $(n + 1)$-ple.

Prove that there is exactly one projective transformation carrying each P_i into Q_i.

3-9 Noncommutativity

This is a brief section describing the main changes that occur if we allow K to be a noncommutative division ring.

Right away we must make a choice between left and right vector spaces, and our choice is left.

The main source of excitement in reviewing §3-1 is that an inspection of Pappus' theorem reveals it to be entirely equivalent to commutativity. Desargues' theorem, on the other hand, goes through unchanged.

Since we have not yet given any attention to Hermitian geometry even in the commutative case, it would be premature to think about noncommutativity as regards inner product spaces.

If we review carefully the treatment of projective geometry, a dominant theme will emerge: inner automorphisms of K have a special role to play.

There is no significant difference in establishing the foundations. V is a left vector space over a division ring K, and Π is the set of all one-dimensional subspaces. When we set up homogeneous coordinates, we note that a point is unchanged when its coordinates are *left-multiplied* by a non-zero element of K. Right-multiplication will usually change the point.

Projective transformations are induced by linear transformations in the same way. One observation to be made is that for a linear transformation T and a scalar multiple cT to induce the same projective transformation c must be in the *center* of K. Thus the projective group of Π is the full linear group of K modulo the non-zero central elements of K.

It is instructive to review Theorem 74. The proof that the four points can be represented as α, β, $\alpha + \beta$ and $k\alpha + \beta$ needs no change. We proceed to the uniqueness. In a second representation we again write $\alpha_0 = r\alpha$, $\beta_0 = s\beta$, $\gamma_0 = \alpha_0 + \beta_0 = r\alpha + s\beta$. The requirement that γ_0 be a left multiple of $\gamma = \alpha + \beta$ again forces $s = r$. So far, all is well. Then $\delta_0 = k_0\alpha_0 + \beta_0 = k_0 r\alpha + r\beta$ and this must be of the form $t\delta = t(k\alpha + \beta)$. Equating coefficients of α and β we find $k_0 r = tk$, $r = t$ and so $k_0 = tkt^{-1}$. We can conclude only that k is unique up to an inner automorphism.

In the same way we see that the existence assertions for projective transformations in Theorem 72 and 75 remain valid, but the uniqueness (Theorems 73 and 76) fails in both cases. In fact, it can be shown that each uniqueness theorem is equivalent to the commutativity of K.

This paragraph is devoted to fulfilling a promise made in §3-5. We are taking V to be a left vector space over K. So the dual V^* is a right vector space over K in the ordinary formulation. However, we are insisting on left vector spaces. So we must reconstrue V^* as a left vector space over the reciprocal division ring K^*. (The reciprocal of a given ring has the same underlying additive abelian group but has the multiplication reversed.)

There exist division rings with K and K^* non-isomorphic. For such a K the planes Π and Π^* will be non-isomorphic.

All this does not in the least spoil the principle of duality, which says that all theorems can be dualized.

We recommend [4] for a very extensive account of the algebra and geometry of projective spaces, with meticulous care paid to the consequences of noncommutativity.

3-10 Synthetic Foundations of Geometry

A proper treatment of the synthetic foundations of geometry would fill a book several times the size of this. All we can do in one section is make an assortment of (we hope) helpful remarks.

(1) *Projective planes* We follow a logical order (but not the historical order) in taking projective spaces as our starting point. And among projective spaces, we take projective planes as our initial target.

It would be just as reasonable to begin with affine planes. At any rate, there is certainly no point in axiomatizing both affine planes and projective planes; the two are readily interchangeable. The choice is largely a matter of taste. Affine planes are closer to our geometric intuition, while projective planes admit axioms of greater symmetry and elegance.

Before we abandon the idea of axioms for an affine plane we make one comment, because of its historical importance, and because it will play a role in our discussion below of Euclidean and non-Euclidean geometry. Among the axioms it is natural to place the celebrated parallel postulate: given a line L and a point P not on it, there exists through P a unique line parallel to L.

A projective plane Π is going to be a set of things called *points*. We now face a second choice: shall the concept of "line" be a second primitive notion, or shall lines be sets of points? I favor sets of points, preferring to have as few primitives as possible. So: in Π we have certain distinguished subsets that we call *lines*. The axioms read:

(a) Any two distinct points lie on exactly one line.

(b) Any two distinct lines meet (necessarily in exactly one point).

The theory can now begin, but there are certain dull extreme cases (like having just one line) which should be excluded. We therefore add a third axiom:

(c) There exist four points, no three of which lie on a line.

This is fine, except that we have spoiled the nice duality that (a) and (b) exhibited. We can restore order rapidly by proving:

(d) There exist four lines, no three of which meet in a point.

Geometry is ready to begin. There is only one trouble. Except for some counting arguments (to which we return below), there are no theorems! We can certainly formulate candidates for theorems. A notable candidate is the theorem of Desargues. It makes sense; it must be true or false. Answer: it may be false. This was first shown in a pioneering paper of Veblen and Wedderburn [37]. At this point we "retreat" to higher-dimensional projective spaces.

(2) *Higher-dimensional projective spaces* I will not select a system of axioms for a general projective space. There has been a lot of variation from one author to another; perhaps the reader would like to experiment on his own. I turn at once to the crucial point: if the dimension is at least 3, Desargues' theorem can be proved and with it (by outright assumption in the plane case) coordinates can be introduced from a division ring. At this point algebra and geometry have merged, and the investigator may use analytic or synthetic methods at his pleasure.

Remark. It is only fair to note that this coordinatization theorem is a substantial piece of mathematics. I imagine that many teachers, exhausted by their labors after coordinatizing Desarguian projective planes, have contented themselves with hand-waving for the higher-dimensional case.

To make the division ring commutative requires, as we know, the theorem of Pappus. It is a charming point that Pappus implies Desargues [18], so for the foundations of commutative linear geometry the theorem of Pappus is all that is needed (on top of the standard axioms).

I mention at this point (for fear of forgetting it altogether) the foundations of inversive geometry. There is a remarkable parallelism, with the theorem of Miquel playing the role of Desargues.

(3) *Non-Desarguian planes* This topic is an active field of research for a large group of mathematicians.

The main interest lies in the finite case. Instructive counting arguments can then be used to show that the number of points on a line is independent of the line and equals the number of lines through any point. If this common number is $n + 1$, we call n the *order* of the plane. The total number of points or lines is $n^2 + n + 1$.

We present a summary of the current state of the art.

(a) If n is a prime power, there is a Desarguian plane of order n based on the finite field with n elements. This of course exhausts the finite Desarguian planes.

(b) A theorem of Bruck and Ryser [7] restricts the possible orders by ruling out those integers $\equiv 1$ or 2 (mod 4) that are not expressible as the sum of two squares. The first few integers ruled out are

$$6, 14, 21, 22, 30, 33$$

The first few that are not prime powers and are not ruled out are

$$10, 12, 14, 15, 18, 20, 24, 26, 28, 34$$

This is exactly where matters stand. It is conceivable at one extreme that all orders allowed by Bruck and Ryser actually have planes. The first mystery is for $n = 10$. At the other extreme it may be that only prime powers are possible. An excellent account of the Bruck-Ryser theorem appears in [16], pp. 394–8.

(c) We now take n to be a prime power, $n = p^k$, and ask for what orders there exist non-Desarguian planes. A first answer is that for $k \geqq 2$ they do exist, except in the cases 4 and 8, which are true exceptions: all planes of orders 4 and 8 are Desarguian.

(d) Lastly let n be a prime. Then only the Desarguian planes are known to exist. For $n = 2, 3, 5$ and 7, the plane has to be Desarguian. For all greater primes the question is open.

It is remarkable how much still remains unknown in this tantalizing subject. For a highly readable introduction to projective planes, [1] is recommended.

(4) *Euclidean and non-Euclidean geometry* We have reserved to the last the foundational aspect of geometry that is most basic of all; how should we proceed to reach ordinary Euclidean geometry, and how do the non-Euclidean geometries fit in?

There is more than one answer. We could take the point of view that dominated our analytic discussion: that projective geometry is the King, and Euclidean geometry at best a Crown Prince. This means we should get all geometries by appropriate modifications of projective geometry. (Or, as an *Erlangen* fanatic would put it, hunt for appropriate subgroups of the projective group.) The procedure then would be to start with a Desarguian projective plane, and add appropriate axioms of order and continuity to force the underlying division ring to be the field of real numbers. Specialize a line at infinity and you get a real affine plane. Select, further, two imaginary points on the line at infinity and you have arrived at the Euclidean plane. This program has been impeccably executed by Coxeter in [9]. (Parenthetical note: faithful to the concept of working within the real framework, Coxeter selects not the circular points at infinity, but the involution on the line at infinity that these ghostly points induce.)

An alternative but entirely equivalent program would start with a Desarguian affine plane; it is noteworthy that the parallel postulate would loom large as an outright unquestioned axiom.

An intermediate step in the program is worthy of attention: drop the Desargues axiom and assume the above-mentioned axioms of order. The result is an ordered affine plane or an ordered projective plane. (It is again a matter of indifference which is being done, since the two theories are equivalent.) No coordinatization being possible, we do not have the algebraic crutch of an ordered division ring to tell us what is going on. We must rely on purely geometric arguments of the type used in the theory of convexity. As an indication of the kind of result that is the objective, we mention the following: any simple closed polygon separates the plane into two sets.

I have not described what is meant by axioms of order here, and would like to discuss the matter briefly. In the affine case the customary method is to use a ternary relation of "betweenness." One's intuition is a fairly good guide to making a selection of axioms and proceeding to the proofs. However, as in often the case with such axiomatics, full execution of the program can be tedious and frustrating.

Comment: we are really talking about linear order on a line, and no one ever had trouble giving axioms for linear order, or proving theorems about it. And yet this is not satisfactory either. We really have two linear orders, one the opposite of the other, and we have no reasonable way of making an arbitrary choice. (We might even find ourselves invoking the axiom of choice in a far-fetched way.)

In teaching the subject I have used an unlovely but quick and effective compromise. I discuss for thirty seconds the way a linear order induces a notion of betweenness, and note that an ordering and its opposite induce the same betweenness. I assume an affine plane where each line possesses such a betweenness. One needs an axiom linking different lines, e.g. the axiom of Pasch. Business can begin.

One more comment is appropriate before we leave this subtopic of order-betweenness axioms. If the selected objective is an ordered projective plane rather than an ordered affine plane, the model we have to imitate is circular order rather than linear order. The axioms and early theorems get a little trickier. We recommend to the reader Coxeter's account in [9], in which there are also references to the earlier literature.

This approach to Euclidean geometry is reasonably efficient and instructive, links up in due course with the standard Euclidean stream of theorems, and (suitably modified) can lead us to the non-Euclidean geometries. But there are overwhelming reasons (historical, philosophical, esthetic, and even mathematical) for not accepting it as the only path. For over two thousand years, Greek geometry, the first real mathematics the human race developed, has fascinated professional and amateur mathematicians. As assembled in Euclid's *Elements*, it is a coherent body of sound mathematics, or more exactly, it can be, as soon as the right axioms are supplied and the proofs patched up a little.

It was not till the end of the 19th century that adequate axioms were set down. (Of course, we should not overlook the possibility that our descendants may find our standards of rigor ludicrous. Some wise man somewhere must have said, "Sufficient unto the day is the rigor thereof.") The project was executed by Hilbert himself, in a book [19] that is devoted mostly to writing down the axioms and discussing them. (But it does not need an entire book to give the axioms. For an excellent telegraphic account, the paper [34] of Tarski is recommended.)

How do the axioms look? They fall into four groups.

I. Incidence. (No parallel postulate, please!)

II. Order-betweenness. We discussed this at some length above.

III. Congruence. This is the decisive feature of Euclidean geometry done in Euclid's style.

Contemporary versions of Euclid's geometry nearly always envisage assigning a real number to each line segment. But the Greeks did not operate that way. For them the key notion was the *equality* of two line segments. In Hilbert's system this gets formulated as a quaternary relation between points A, B, C, D, intended to signify $AB = CD$. A small set of skillfully selected axioms does the trick.

Hilbert added a second group of congruence axioms that apply to angles. This added considerable technical complication, for the handling of angles in Euclidean geometry is a little delicate. Later authors made a perceptible improvement when they *defined* congruence of angles in terms of congruence of line segments.

IV. A lot of theorems can be proved on the basis of the first three groups of axioms. But we fall short of the decisive theorems, and certainly remain some distance from characterizing the Euclidean plane.

The final axiom is an appropriate assumption of *continuity*. (It is customary to remark that without such an axiom there is trouble in the very first proposition in the very first book of Euclid—the inter-secting of two circles to construct an equilateral triangle.)

At this point, if we ignore the parallel postulate for the moment, it can at last be announced that we are ready to construct the entire edifice of Euclid's geometry. And the best way to sustain the claim is to do it. Forder [12] and Borsuk and Szmielew [6] are recommended references where you can see the enterprise carried out with diligence and skill.

But we must return to the point we have treated inadequately: the role of the parallel postulate. Here we marvel at the genius of Euclid (or some unknown predecessor whom he quoted), for the parallel postulate indeed deserves to be segregated, assumed reluctantly, and denied experimentally.

The facts are as follows: the axioms listed above (without the parallel postulate) have exactly two models. If we assert that through each point not on a line there is a unique parallel to the line, we get the Euclidean plane. If we deny this it turns out that there are infinitely many parallels, and we get a unique object called the *hyperbolic* plane, discovered inde-pendently by Lobachevski and Bolyai, although foreshadowed by Saccheri and (perhaps) Gauss.

An informed reader may be wondering where elliptic geometry got lost in the shuffle. The answer lies in our choice of order axioms. If we pick them so as to allow *either* linear order or cylic order and leave all other axioms unchanged, we find exactly one more model. It is obtained by denying the parallel postulate in favor of the assertion that there are no parallel lines at all.

There is a simple model for the elliptic plane. Take the usual two-sphere in three-dimensional Euclidean space, and let the lines be great circles. Use the usual distances (measured along great circles) and angles of spherical geometry. The result verifies all the Hilbert axioms, except that we have an infinite number of lines through any two antipodal points. But this is easily remedied: change the space by identifying every point with its antipodal point. When we do this we reach our old friend, the real projective plane, making a repeat performance equipped with a distance and an angle that convert it into one of the two non-Euclidean planes.

No one should be surprised to learn that this elliptic distance is really a cross ratio, defined relative to an imaginary conic. Angle is also a cross ratio, but the right remark to make is that distance and angle are in perfect duality in elliptic geometry.

We close this survey with a full return to the projective plane. The hyperbolic plane can also be viewed projectively: specialize a (real) conic in the real projective plane, keep only the points inside it, and define distance and angle by appropriate cross ratios.

APPENDIX

Topological Aspects of Projective Spaces

If K is a topological division ring, the projective spaces defined over K yield interesting examples of topological spaces. This appendix is devoted to a sketch, with no attempt at completeness or precision, of their topological properties.

With ambitious generality we start with K an arbitrary topological division ring. First we look at $V_n(K)$, an n-dimensional left vector space over K. We view it as the product of n copies of K, and award it the Cartesian product topology, noting that the result is independent of the choice of basis.

When K is the field R of real numbers, $V_n(R)$ is the familiar n-dimensional Euclidean space. For many purposes, topologists dismiss it with the remark that it is contractible and thus has the homotopy type of a point.

In this appendix we shall use the notation $P_n(K)$ for n-dimensional projective space over K. When we drape the projective space $P_n(K)$ around $V_n(K)$ we get a topological object more worthy of scrutiny. Our first problem is to topologize $P_n(K)$. This could be done by adjoining to the affine space $V_n(K)$ a suitable hyperplane at infinity, but it is awkward to describe the topology in these terms. Instead let us take as our guide the procedure used in describing a manifold by overlapping neighborhoods. Think of $P_n(K)$ as $(n + 1)$-ples of elements of K, where only the ratios count. Let W_i be the set of $(n + 1)$-ples that have 1 in the i-th coordinate but are otherwise unrestricted. Then W_i looks like $V_n(K)$ and we topologize it that way. The projective space $P_n(K)$ is covered by the affine spaces $W_1, \cdots, W_{n+1}$. We topologize $P_n(K)$ by declaring each of the W_i's to be open.

Remark. We note at this point that a similar procedure is feasible in algebraic geometry. One first defines affine varieties, then general varieties by suitably pasting together affine ones. The role of compactness is played by an appropriate assumption of completeness. The space $P_n(K)$ is the motivating example of a complete variety.

If the topological division ring K is locally compact, obviously the same is true for $V_n(K)$ and then for $P_n(K)$. If K is non-discrete, more is true: $P_n(K)$ is compact. We sketch the proof, using the known fact that there exists a real-valued norm $|x|$ on K that gives the topology, is multiplicative ($|xy| = |x|\,|y|$), and has the property that bounded closed sets are compact. This time we cover $P_n(K)$ by the sets $Y_1, \cdots, Y_{n+1}$ where in Y_i the i-th coordinate is 1 and all coordinates have norm ≤ 1. Clearly the Y_i's are compact. We see that they cover $P_n(K)$ by dividing each $(n + 1)$-ple by the coordinate of largest norm.

A topological division ring is either connected or totally disconnected. In the locally compact totally disconnected case, $P_n(K)$ is uninteresting as a topological space; it is compact, separable, totally disconnected, and without isolated points, and hence is homeomorphic to the Cantor set.

And so after this brief flirtation with general division rings we retreat to the reals, complexes, and quaternions (the only connected locally compact division rings). We shall use for them the notations R, C, and Q.

We wish to have a more economical presentation of the projective spaces over R, C, and Q. We treat the three uniformly by using $|x|$ for the absolute value in all cases. (In the case of the quaternions it is usually called the norm.) We normalize the $(n + 1)$-ples used by requiring

$$(48) \qquad |x_1|^2 + \cdots + |x_{n+1}|^2 = 1$$

After this we still have equivalence classes:

$$(x_1, \cdots, x_{n+1}) \sim (ax_1, \cdots, ax_{n+1})$$

with a now confined to elements satisfying $|a| = 1$.

(*Note*: in the case of the quaternions we must be careful to use only *left* multiplication by a.)

We think of the setup we have reached in the following terms. The points satisfying (48) form a sphere of dimension $k(n + 1) - 1$, where $k = 1, 2,$ or 4 according as we are dealing with R, C, or Q. This sphere is acted on by the group of elements of absolute value 1 in R, C, or Q. For R this group consists of ± 1 and is describable as the zero-dimensional sphere S_0; for C it consists of the complex numbers of absolute value 1, the circle group S_1; for Q it consists of the quaternions of norm 1 and is a three-sphere S_3. (This group is the covering group of the orthogonal group in three variables.)

A shorthand description is given by $P_n(R) = S_n/S_0$, $P_n(C) = S_{2n+1}/S_1$, $P_n(Q) = S_{4n+3}/S_3$.

We shall discuss the individual cases in greater detail. The identification made in passing from the n-sphere S_n to n-dimensional real projective space $P_n(R)$ is particularly easy to visualize: one identifies each point of S_n with its opposite or antipodal point. We can get a representation with less duplication if we think of S_n divided into a northern and a southern hemisphere. We throw away the southern hemisphere. What we have left is the northern hemisphere plus the equator, and we still have to identify antipodal points on the equator. As a further simplification squash the hemisphere down flat. Now we have an n-disc (or solid n-sphere) with antipodal points of the boundary identified.

In particular the real projective plane is a disc with opposite points of the boundary identified. Instead of taking the boundary as a circle, we could make it a square. Then the necessary identifications are of the opposite sides of the square, as indicated by the arrows in the figures. It is interesting to compare the identifications that create the torus and Klein bottle, and the partial identifications that create the cylinder and Möbius strip. Note that by making a suitable cut in the real projective plane, starting at some point and cutting around and back to the starting point, we can leave it in one piece; that piece is a Möbius strip.

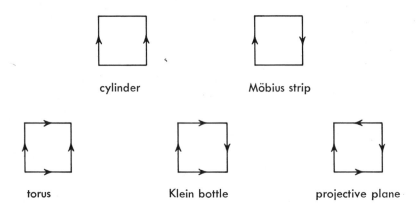

cylinder   Möbius strip

torus   Klein bottle   projective plane

$P_n(R)$ is orientable for n odd, and non-orientable for n even. If a monster living on an even-dimensional sphere is subjected to the antipodal map, he switches from right-handed to left-handed. (You can see this explicitly on the 2-sphere.) So after the identification takes place, the monsters living on $P_{2m}(R)$ have no consistent way of deciding who is right-handed. Algebraically, the antipodal map on the n-sphere is implemented by the $n + 1 \times n + 1$ diagonal matrix with $- 1$'s on the diagonal, and its determinant is $- 1$ for n even, 1 for n odd. Thus it reverses or maintains the orientation of the n-sphere according as n is even or odd.

The complex projective line simply adds a point at infinity to the affine line. The latter is Euclidean 2-space. Adding a point at infinity compactifies it to the 2-sphere, called the *Riemann sphere* in this case. The complex projective plane adds a Riemann sphere at infinity to Euclidean 4-space.

The other description of the complex projective line and plane goes as follows. It is possible to map S_3 onto $P_1(C) = S_2$, and S_5 onto $P_2(C)$, in such a way that the inverse image of every point is a circle. This is a *fibering* of S_3 and S_5 by S_1. It is not a direct product; the circles get twisted as they wander through the total space. Since the fibering arises from the action of a group, the object we get is a special lind of fiber bundle called a *principal bundle*.

The higher complex projective spaces and the quaternionic projective spaces can be described similarly. Incidentally, all these spaces are orientable.

The most important invariants of a topological space are its homology and cohomology groups. Let us ignore the trivial dimension 0. Then for both homology and cohomology with integer coefficients we have the following values:

$$P_n(C): Z \text{ in dimensions } 2, 4, \cdots, 2n$$

$$P_n(Q): Z \text{ in dimensions } 4, 8, \cdots, 4n$$

and 0 otherwise. (Z denotes the integers and Z_2 below, the integers mod 2.)

For cohomology there is a ring structure and it is of the simplest kind. With x a generator in the lowest dimension, we get the powers x^2, x^3, $\cdots$ up to x_n, and higher powers are 0.

For the real projective spaces the results are more complicated. We content ourselves with listing the homology groups with integral coefficients.

$$P_{2k}(R): Z_2 \text{ in dimensions } 1, 3, 5, \cdots, 2k - 1$$

$$P_{2k+1}(R): Z_2 \text{ in dimensions } 1, 3, 5, \cdots, 2k - 1$$

$$Z \text{ in dimension } 2k + 1$$

We note one standard application: for the even-dimensional real projective spaces (including the real projective plane) the Lefschetz fixed point theorem tells us that any continuous map has a fixed point.

In concluding we mention that there is precisely one more projective space of topological significance: the Cayley plane.

First let us give the algebraic background. Assume that a projective plane satisfies not Desargues' theorem but one of its consequences: the *uniqueness* of the construction of a fourth harmonic point in Fig. 21, page 110. Then it was proved by Ruth Moufang that coordinates can be introduced that take values in a type of slightly non-associative ring called a Cayley division ring. Such a ring is an eight-dimensional algebra over a field, and exists over suitable base fields, for example the real numbers. The real Cayley plane obtained this way is a 16-dimensional manifold, with homology or cohomology groups Z, Z in dimensions 8 and 16.

BIBLIOGRAPHY

1. A. A. ALBERT, "Symmetric and alternate matrices in an arbitrary field," *Trans. Amer. Math. Soc.* 43(1938), 386–436.

2. A. A. ALBERT and R. SANDLER, *An Introduction to Finite Projective Planes*, Holt, Rinehart and Winston, New York, 1968.

3. C. ARF, "Unterschungen über quadratische Formen in Körpern der Charakteristick 2 (Teil I)," *J. für reine und angew. Math.* 183(1940), 148–167.

4. R. BAER, *Linear Algebra and Projective Geometry*, Academic Press, New York, 1952.

5. K. BORSUK and W. SZMIELEW, *Foundations of Geometry*, North-Holland, Amsterdam, 1960.

6. N. BOURBAKI, *Formes Sesquilinéaires et Formes Quadratiques*, Hermann, Paris, 1959.

7. R. H. BRUCK and H. J. RYSER, "The non-existence of certain finite projective planes," *Can. J. of Math.* 1(1949), 88–93.

8. H. S. M. COXETER, *Non-Euclidean Geometry*, 3rd ed., Toronto, 1957.

9. ———, *The Real Projective Plane*, 2nd ed., McGraw-Hill, New York, 1959.

10. M. DEURING, "Galoische Theorie und Darstellungstheorie," *Math. Annalen* 107(1933), 140–4.

11. C. J. EVERETT and H. RYSER, "Rational vector spaces I," *Duke Math. J.* 16(1949), 553–570.

12. H. G. FORDER, *The Foundations of Euclidean Geometry*, Cambridge, 1927.

13. H. GROSS and R. D. ENGLE, "Bilinear forms on k-vectorspaces of denumerable dimension in the case of char(k) = 2," *Comment. Math. Helv.* 40(1966), 247–266.

14. H. GROSS and H. R. FISCHER, "Non-real fields k and infinite dimensional k vectorspaces," *Math. Ann.* 159(1965), 285–308.

15. K. W. GRUENBERG and A. J. WEIR, *Linear Geometry*, Van Nostrand, Princeton, 1967.

16. M. HALL, *The Theory of Groups*, Macmillan, New York, 1959.

17. P. R. HALMOS, *Finite-dimensional Vector Spaces*, Van Nostrand, Princeton, 1958.

18. G. HESSENBERG, "Beweis des Desarguesschen Satzes aus dem Pascalschen," *Math. Ann.* 61(1905), 161–172.

19. D. HILBERT, *Grundlagen der Geometrie*, 7th ed., Leipzig, 1930.

20. N. JACOBSON, *Lectures on Abstract Algebra, Vol. II*, Van Nostrand, Princeton, 1953.

21. B. W. JONES, *The Arithmetic Theory of Quadratic Forms*, Carus Monograph no. 10, New York, 1950.

22. I. KAPLANSKY, "Elementary divisors and modules," *Trans. Amer. Math. Soc.* 66(1949), 464–491.

23. ———, "Forms in infinite-dimensional spaces," *Anais Acad. Bras. Cien.* 22(1950), 1–17.

24. ———, "Representations of separable algebras," *Duke Math. J.* 19(1952), 219–222.

25. ———, "Products of normal operators, "*Duke Math. J.* 20(1953), 257–260.

26. I. KAPLANSKY and R. J. SHAKER, "Abstract quadratic forms," *Can. J. of Math.*

27. S. LANG, "On quasi-algebraic closure," *Ann. of Math.* 55(1952), 373–390.

28. S. MAC LANE and G. BIRKHOFF, *Algebra*, Macmillan, New York, 1967.

29. T. O'MEARA, *Introduction to Quadratic Forms*, Springer, Berlin, 1963.

30. G. PALL, "Hermitian quadratic forms in a quasi-field," *Bull. Amer. Math. Soc.* 51(1945), 889–893.

31. C. PEARCY, "A complete set of unitary invariants for operators generating finite W^*-algebras of type I," *Pac. J. of Math.* 12(1962), 1405–1414.

32. L. J. SAVAGE, "The application of vectorial methods to metric geometry," *Duke Math. J.* 13(1946), 521–8.

33. W. SPECHT, "Zur Theorie der Matrixen II," *Jahresber. D. Math. Ver.* 50(1940), 19–23.

34. A. TARSKI, "What is elementary geometry?" Pp. 16–29 of Proc. Int. Sympos. held at Berkeley 1957–8. North-Holland, Amsterdam, 1959.

35. O. TAUSSKY and H. ZASSENHAUS, "On the similarity transformation between a matrix and its transpose," *Pac. J. of Math.* 9(1959), 893–6.

36. O. VEBLEN and P. FRANKLIN, "On matrices whose elements are integers," *Ann. of Math.* 23(1921), 1–15.

37. O. VEBLEN and J. H. MACLAGLAN-WEDDERBURN, "Non-desarguesian and non-pascalian geometries," *Trans. Amer. Math. Soc.* 8(1907), 379–388.

38. A. VOSS, "Zur Theorie der orthogonalen Substitutionen," *Math. Ann.* 13(1878), 320–374.

39. C. T. C. WALL, "Quadratic forms on finite groups, and related topics," *Topology* 2(1963), 253–261.

40. G. E. WALL, "On the conjugacy classes in the unitary, symplectic, and orthogonal groups," *J. Australian Math. Soc.* 3(1963), 1–62.

41. N. A. WIEGMANN, "Normal products of matrices," *Duke Math. J.* 15(1948), 633–8.

42. E. P. WIGNER, "On weakly positive matrices," *Can. J. of Math.* 15(1963), 313–7.

43. E. WITT, "Theorie der quadratischen Formen in beliebigen Körpern," *J. für reine und angew. Math.* 176(1937), 31–44.

INDEX